OUTPATIENTS DEPARTMENT

PITAL

NURSING SISTER
AND TRAINEES

JUNGLE DOCTOR OPERATES

JUNGLE DOCTOR PULLS A LEG

PAUL WHITE

JUNGLE DOCTOR
PULLS A LEG

With Nineteen Illustrations
by Graham Wade

THE PATERNOSTER PRESS

Made and Printed in Great Britain for
The Paternoster Press, Paternoster House,
3 Mount Radford Crescent, Exeter, Devon
by Cox & Wyman, Limited
London, Fakenham and Reading

TO
DAPHNE ROSE
A "FUNDI" IN TURNING BARRIERS
INTO BRIDGES

CONTENTS

CHAPTER I

SLIPPERY START

THE umbrella turned inside out. A jagged flash of lightning revealed Mboga splashing up to the hospital door.

I nudged Daudi. "Sorry about the loss of your umbrella, Mboga; you mustn't be upset. Think rather of the crops and the harvest and this magnificent rain."

Daudi grinned as Mboga wiped water out of his eyes and said slyly, "I will have courage, Bwana. What makes this less difficult is the thought that it was your umbrella." Solemnly he handed me the wreckage.

I smiled. "If this is all the damage it won't be so bad. Last year the first storm of the rainy season brought us a cracked skull and two broken arms."

Daudi stood up and peered out into the darkness. "It was a night very much like this. *Kah!* How would you like to make a *safari* on foot tonight?"

Mboga rolled his eyes as again lightning flashed blindingly. Daudi's voice was half blotted out by the crash of thunder. All I heard was "... Look!"

We peered over his shoulder, but the night was dark as pitch. Again for a split second forked lightning turned the landscape

9

into a vivid black-and-white picture. Two men were struggling
up the hill. One of them was Gideon, who ran the local bus.

"*Heeh!*" said Mboga, "that second man is Malatu. He
comes from Kongwa. *Heeh!* A man of strength—he can carry
a load on his shoulders as big as a man."

Daudi opened the door. Light flooded through. Squelching
through the rain came the two figures, broad smiles on their
faces. "*Hodi?*—May we come in?" shouted Gideon above the
noise of the rain.

"*Karibu*—come in."

He shook his head. "*Ng'o*, perhaps it is better for you to
come outside—all of you—and to come fast."

"Outside? *Hongo!*—Why?"

"My bus is three miles away, on the far side of much flood
water. In it is Petro. . . ."

Malatu broke in. "Your Petro with the swollen feet who was
lent to our hospital for a year. He walked miles to our village
because of the illness of his child, and behold, he was gripped
by sickness. The best way to help was to cause him to arrive
here, so I carried him on my shoulders till we came to the
road—*Yoh!* a *safari* of many miles through much water and
more mud." He rubbed his neck, and then went on, "We were
given a ride in the lorry of Suliman, the Indian, but behold, on
the way we overtook Gideon here, and we have come with
speed until. . . ." He pointed with his chin into the darkness.

"*Heeh!*" grinned Gideon, "and even if my bus were a ship it
could not have finished the journey. But we can still bring
Petro to hospital tonight if we travel with care. I will make the
preparations." He hurried off in the direction of his home.

I turned to Malatu. "What's wrong with Petro?"

"His legs swell, Bwana. His body shakes with fever. He says
there is poison in his blood. We started yesterday soon after
sunrise, and behold, for more than a day we have travelled
with difficulty to come forty miles."

Gideon came hurrying back carrying a coil of rope and an
inflated inner tube from his truck.

Daudi and I pressed ahead in the darkness through the rain
and the flooded river to the bus. Inside, covered by a soaking
overcoat, lay a very sick Petro. His pulse raced; he had a high
fever. Daudi pulled the coat back, and revealed an ugly egg-
sized swelling on his shin. It dwarfed the other lumps which

had made Petro lame for years. I lifted the sick man's head. "Petro, swallow these. . . ."

His eyes opened, his mouth followed suit, and down went the capsules. Slowly he took in the surroundings. "*Kah!* Bwana, I have been sleeping."

"Truly, but this is no place to sleep. We have a safari of no small difficulty before us. It is a thing of importance that you should be in bed, and warm, so that we may fight your sickness with wisdom. But between us and those lights that you see on the hill is a distance of three miles, and the place of danger has water up to my armpits; water that moves with speed."

Petro's teeth chattered, "*Kah!* I cannot swim!"

"Can you use your feet at all, Petro?"

"*Ng'o.* They have been refusing to walk these days, Bwana. Also, *kumbe!* they have no joy in cold water."

A good half mile away we could see a light swinging to and fro, and soon Malatu came up to us carrying a lantern and the coil of rope. "Carry this, Bwana. I'll carry him. Gideon comes with the truck tube."

The water was knee deep as we started our safari back.

A hundred yards ahead of us a torch beam shone and Mboga's voice yelled, "Over this way!"

Fast-moving brown water banked up around our legs. The path was dangerously slippery. A figure loomed up out of the darkness. It was Gideon, holding above his head the blown up tube, which looked like a king-sized lifebuoy.

"Put Petro into this," he shouted.

Daudi and I did so. "Gently now," roared Gideon. "We'll tie short ropes to it. Malatu, you stand here and hold this end of the long rope. Mboga has the other end. He is by the *majifu* bushes on the other side of the deepest channel. Daudi and I will walk each side of Petro and float him across, while you keep his head above water, Bwana."

"*Hongo!*" shivered Petro, "remember, my nose breathes better above water."

"*Kumbe!*" came Daudi's voice in my ear. "We must travel with care. He could be drowned in a minute in this fierceness of water."

We set Petro as comfortably as we could through the centre of the tube, and struggled on through the swirling water. It was a comfort to see the light on the far side of the flood, and to feel the steady pull on the rope coming from that direction.

We came to a shallower place. "Things are going pretty well, Daudi," I shouted.

"*Eheh!*" he gulped as water splashed into his face. "But be careful. There are some big holes about here. They . . ."

Unexpectedly my head disappeared beneath the surface. I was tossed downstream like a cork until my hand grasped the branch of a small tree. I came gasping to the surface.

"Is everything all right with Petro?"

"*Eheh!*" shouted Daudi.

I battled upstream and found myself above our makeshift ambulance. In turning, both my feet slipped. It was like being shot out of a catapult. Then I was pulled up with a jerk—my head completely under water. I swam a couple of strokes and surfaced. Petro's voice came, "*Yoh-heeh!* I have him by the leg!"

"*Heeh!*" I spluttered. "You have indeed!"

"*Kah!*" came Daudi's voice, full of laughter, "it's not many who have the opportunity of pulling the Bwana's leg."

"*Hongo!*" groaned Malatu as we struggled up the hill to the hospital, "My legs have within them the strong desire to cramp."

"Have no fear," said Daudi. "We have the answer to that. Cramps have no teeth while we have a bottle of bitter-tasting pills in the cupboard."

"My legs," grunted Gideon, "have a high desire to fall off. *Kumbe!* I'm tired beyond all words."

"Speaking of legs," came Petro's faint voice, "I would willingly exchange mine with anybody. But be careful before you agree. They will not work if you try to walk on them. Stand on them and they ache without stopping. Lie on them and they throb. And bump them! *Heeh!* It is strong pain. *Kumbe!* They aren't even food for the eye to look at."

"*Hongo!*" came Malatu's tired voice, "you'd be better without them." Then, realizing what he'd said, he clamped his hand over his mouth.

"You have spoken words of great truth," muttered Petro. "*Koh!*" he turned to me, "Bwana, if I ever needed the help of medicines and doctors who operate, it's these days."

.   .   .   .   .

"*Yoh-heeh!*" said Mboga, as he put the thermometer into Petro's mouth, "Last night we had food for the memory."

Baruti drummed on his plaster-covered leg. "Tell us."

Mboga took out the thermometer, read it without moving a muscle, and started. "Petro was sitting in one of the tubes from Gideon's large truck—you know how big it is! He sat through the hole in the middle and we pulled him across the river. All was well until the Bwana disappeared ... splash! gulp! But before you could breathe twice, there he was amongst the bushes. He struggled to his feet and we could see his head moving towards us with water splashing over it. He found a shallow place, stepped over the rope, and was bending down to hold the tube steady when the mud deceived his feet and ... he was gone again!"

Petro's voice came weakly, "I was not sitting on that tube, but THROUGH it, and *yoh!* I was kicked! I put out my hand, and there was the Bwana's leg, so I grabbed it!"

"*Eheh!*" chuckled Baruti, "and held his head under?"

"A little only," whispered Petro. "He swam, his head came up, his legs went down, and behold, we were soon over on the other bank."

I stood beside Petro's bed. Mboga silently passed the thermometer to me. It read 103.4°.

"So far, it's a case of too much water outside and not enough inside, Petro. *Eheh!* And you must have more pills. Drink plenty of fluid—even more than I swallowed in that river—and take the pills every four hours, day and night. Now for your legs."

B

Mali, the nurse in charge of the ward, drew back the blankets, and I looked at a pair of legs which were no strangers to me. Years ago I had first seen them when Petro had been carried in by a group of reluctant relatives who had demanded a cow for their labours. Mali handed me a card. It was dated seven years back:

PETRO CHILANGO. DISEASE: MADURA FOOT.

I remembered vividly his painful, swollen feet, gnarled and warty like artichokes. I glanced at the card; the tests we had made were all recorded with their results, and at the bottom was the ominous verdict: "AMPUTATION RECOMMENDED". I looked down at Petro, remembering the day we had spoken together about this. His reply had been full of steady faith, "Bwana, let us give God a chance first. Maybe He will choose to make them better. . . ."

We had used all available treatments—hot foot-baths, injections, and scores of bottles of medicine. Six months went by and he had not stirred out of bed. His legs were no worse, but they certainly were not even the slightest bit better. The one thing that happened was that a change came over the whole ward. Petro, sitting there in bed, had been, as someone put it, "Like a lamp with a trimmed wick, and a glass that had no soot upon it." He had been a burning and a shining light for God.

While these thoughts were going through my mind I was automatically examining his leg. The hot area on the back of his heel was spreading, and under his knee there was a hard swelling. I listened to his chest, and then sat down, covering up his legs.

"It is even as I thought, Petro. Germs have entered your body from your inflamed foot. They have attacked the veins under your knee."

The sick man spoke quietly, "There is no way to help me? They have to go?"

I nodded.

"When?"

"Petro," I spoke more slowly than usual, "it's not your legs only that I'm worried about; it's your life!"

A slow, weary smile came over the African's good-looking face. "*Heeh!* Bwana!" he sighed, "there are times when it would be a comfort to leave this body behind, and go straight through to be with Jesus."

"Supposing God has more for you to do in this life?"

"What can I do?" he asked bitterly. "My days are full of pain. I can't even think clearly." He made a despairing movement with his hands. "Bwana, I'm only a burden. I have had words of hot anger with Hewa and her relations. They say, what use is a man who cannot walk? They say it again and again . . . there is truth in their words! If my legs must go, that is worse still. It's better for me to die."

"Do not try to make decisions when you are tired or sick or angry, Petro. What we must do now is fight these *dudus* in your body before we do anything for your legs. And the first thing is rest—and plenty of it."

Mali handed me some pills. "Here they are, one for the germs, one for the pain and one for sleep."

Petro slowly lifted himself up on his elbow. He took the pills and swallowed them. "Thank you, Bwana." He sank back on the pillow. Then in a voice that only I could hear, "*Kah!* it is easy to tangle your thoughts when your leg throbs and keeps on throbbing, and a helper of Shaitan the Devil comes and spends his time telling you with each throb of pain, 'God doesn't care. God doesn't care'. . . ."

"The answer to that, Petro, is simple. Don't be polite to the devil—tell him he is a liar."

He smiled bleakly. "I'll tell him, Bwana."

When I finished my round I moved quietly to Petro's bed. He was asleep. One arm lay over the edge of the bed and on the floor his Bible was open where it had fallen. I picked it up. A verse was underlined and I read, 'Happy is the man whose strength is in Thee; the man who when he passes through the valley of tears, uses it for a well'.

I remembered the last time Petro had been a patient; the valley of tears had been very real in those days, but Petro had "filled his water bottle" in that valley, and many had been refreshed. As I gently lifted his arm and tucked the blanket around him I prayed, "Lord, help him to fill his water bottle again, *this* time."

.   .   .   .   .

Baruti hobbled down the path from the hospital early next morning, using a broom for a crutch. He paused outside my door. "*Hodi*, Bwana?"

"*Karibu*—come in. *Habari*, Baruti?"

"The news is good, but Petro slept badly and Mwendwa says his temperature is higher and that his stomach had no joy in the medicine. Listen, Bwana, his troubles are many, and they are not only his feet, but his family. You heard him say he had words of strong anger with his wife and her family? Bwana, listen to *my* words."

I grinned. Baruti had his own way of telling things. He could never start a story in the middle—he was certain to re-travel every step of the road. I sat down beside him, prepared to listen. He started:

"Ihowe, the crow, had been invited to two feasts. Hyæna had said to him, 'Near the buyu tree at the hour of sunset there will be food that will bring joy to your beak. Come with appetite when you hear the beating of the drums.' Hyæna had scarcely walked away when Jackal and two members of his tribe came along and said, 'Good-day, Crow, today at the time when the clouds become red there will be a *sikuku* under the shadow of the kuyu tree. When you hear the drums beat, come with an expectant stomach.'

"Crow's mind was full of the comforting thoughts of food, and as the sun went on its journey he walked through the jungle looking at the kuyu tree, which was north, and at the buyu tree, which was south. He came to a place where the road forked. On the right hand it went to the kuyu tree, on the left hand it went to the buyu tree. He heard the drums of the hyænas calling him. His right foot stepped along the path that led in that direction. His inner crow told him of his need. He looked towards the place where hyænas ate flesh with enthusiasm. His right leg moved further down this path. But he turned his head in the other direction for the sound of the drums of the jackals was louder. His left leg moved in that direction. Hunger rumbled within him. . . ."

I chuckled. "Go on, Baruti. Tell me what happened. I know you will have at least six different yarns why he took a bit bigger step to the right, and why he took a bit bigger step to the left."

Baruti nodded quietly. "*Heeh*, Bwana, but such was the

wisdom of crow that he could not decide which way to go; he could not make up his mind, and the strain was too great and he was torn in two pieces!"

"Horrid yarn before breakfast. Come with me to the hospital."

Baruti limped along beside me. "Bwana, think again of the whole matter. You remember when Petro married he had no interest in the ways of God. He lived in a way that caused much talking behind hands. He chose his wife because she danced those dances which face towards lust and not towards laughter. *Kumbe!* And she brewed beer with a skill that brought much praise from her uncle Miti. You remember that when Petro heard the words of God he chose to travel God's way—uphill, and that Hewa followed him, but with only half her mind? And though we all prayed with strength that she would follow whole-heartedly the ways of God, she hasn't. It is as though she has one foot in Petro's house and one foot in the house of her relations. And *kumbe!* They are a family of trouble."

"The medicine man, Miti, we know only too well, Baruti. What an uncle to have!"

"She has another who is little better, Kuguni, the Bug."

"Before Petro first came to the hospital, wasn't there a story of the tragic death of his small daughter?"

Baruti nodded. "Behold, Hewa went on a visit to her uncle's house. They were brewing beer in a great clay pot. There was a quarrel. The pot was pushed over and the child, Lutu, was scalded with boiling beer, and died from very bad burns. In those days the words of Miti were that spells had been cast against Hewa and Petro because he had turned his back on the old ways. Miti said he could have protected them with charms, but . . ."

Baruti shrugged his shoulders.

"That was years ago. For a long time Hewa had sadness because she was childless. We gave her many injections and then Aramu was born."

He nodded. "There has been quietness till these days when Hewa went with little Aramu to visit more of her relations. He became ill with a great cough like the song of *nzogolo*—the rooster; it was as though someone choked him, and his nose bled and his eyes went red."

"Probably whooping-cough, Baruti. An ugly disease unless you treat it fast and thoroughly."

"That was the beginning of this matter. It was only when they feared the child would die that they called Petro. That very day the dry season broke in that part of the country. There was no way to travel but on foot and Petro walked miles on those dreadful feet with worry in his head and anger in his heart. There was a quarrel and strong words. Petro blamed Hewa for not taking the boy to hospital, and for using charms and native medicines. Hewa screamed at him. The knowing ones of her family looked for an excuse for the child not re-covering—even as they did when Lutu died—so again they started the rumour that Petro had made trouble and a spell had been cast." Baruti shrugged. "Hewa has run away and taken the sick child with her. Petro doesn't know where they are, and. . . ."

I finished for him, "And Petro blames himself?"

Baruti nodded. "That is the difficulty."

We came into the ward and stood at the end of Petro's bed. He was exhausted. "It's no good, Bwana," he muttered, "I can't keep the medicines down. I feel as though I'm on fire, and my head won't work. And the pain. . . ."

"We'll fix that problem with some penicillin injections, Petro. Lie quietly." I turned to Mwendwa, "Give him a million units at once, please."

CHAPTER II

MOSI

"*Heeh!*" said Baruti, "look, there is nobody in the bed next to Petro."

Mali hurried over. "Please talk outside. Petro's very ill. He's asleep now and I went him to stay asleep."

Baruti moved to the door as quietly as his plaster-covered leg would allow. After him came Daudi and Tembo. "*Kah!*" said the former, "there is one whom I would like to have in that bed, now. His name is Juma Mosi, Saturday; Mosi for short. He's about fourteen. His legs are twisted, and he's so thin that his bones stick through him."

Tembo opened his eyes wide. "*Heeh!* That's how I was when I first came to the hospital!"

"You were indeed."

Tembo flexed his muscles and a big smile spread over his face. "*Eheh*, it's different now."

Daudi went on. "Mosi has many troubles to be found and treated, but everything depends on having him in hospital. The big problem is his father. They call him Kibiriti, Matches, for his anger easily bursts into flame."

"*Hongo!*" said Tembo, "is he then like the rhinoceros, who has red eyes and who rushes about doing things in great anger?"

"*Eheh*," smiled Baruti, "he certainly does this, and when his temper fills his head then wisdom disappears and he does things that often he has sorrow about later. He has beaten the boy dangerously more than once."

"*Eheh*, all that is true," said Daudi. "Mosi is very ill, but when anyone says take him to the hospital, his father has great anger and screams, 'No! No! No!'"

"What can we do about it, Daudi?"

"There is a way. These days a new African District Commissioner has come to Dodoma. He could help us, for a very special reason: when he was a schoolboy he had an accident to his eye with an arrow . . ."

"Not that nimble-minded boy whom I called Nelson after the Admiral of long ago who had only one eye?"

"It is he, Bwana. He had an excellent education, went to an English University, visited India, and many other places, and now he is a person of importance, doing the work that was done before by an English District Officer."

"Do you think he could control this angry man, Daudi?"

"I think he would find a way, Bwana, and the news is that he will pass this way today."

Baruti turned to Tembo. "This is a thing of importance. Sit on the Great Stone and watch the road with open eyes. If you see the car coming let us know." The boy ran off, and a few minutes later Baruti strolled down to help him with his road watching.

Right through the morning I could hear Baruti's *ilimba* playing on and on, then it abruptly stopped and Tembo came tearing up to Daudi. Soon afterwards a Land Rover drove up to the hospital and a young man in a white Palm Beach suit came across to me. In faultless English he said, "Good morning, Doctor."

"Good morning," I replied.

He said, "May I introduce myself? I am one of the new District Commissioners. My name is Nelson Kolongo."

We shook hands. "Welcome, Bwana D.C." As I looked at him it was very hard to tell that his left eye was glass.

He smiled at me. "I've been here before, Doctor."

I switched my language into Chigogo and said, "*Koh!* Do you think I would forget my friend who came in here with great damage to his eye, and one who found himself in great trouble when he raided the brown sugar tin?"

Mr. Kolongo laughed. "Truly your memory has strength."

"That may be, but I'm delighted to know that you are now in an administrative position."

He looked at me very quietly and said, "There is great responsibility on the shoulders of those of us who have had opportunities, and there is work to do these days in our country." He paused. "One thing I will never forget about my stay in hospital is the misery I felt when I first walked up that path."

"You certainly had a terrible eye."

"And I had a terrible pain, Doctor. One eye was blind and the other one was nearly so. My father would not agree to my coming to the hospital. The chief of our village spoke loud words, but did nothing. My pain grew worse and blindness came closer, but you heard about my troubles. You arranged things with the District Officer—an Englishman of understanding; and did he not come to our village and speak with strength—and so I came to the hospital!"

"Yes, but we had to remove the damaged eye, or you would have lost the sight of the other."

Nelson Kolongo nodded his head. "What I heard and saw in hospital have remained in my memory. I went back to school, and then to the University. Then came this special opportunity. I have a job to do in my own country and I shall do it, I hope, as well as the Englishmen who were here before. After all, being an African makes it easier to understand the thinking of my people."

"That is why I interrupted your *safari*. At the village of Mpuguzi there is a very sick boy, Juma Mosi. His father refuses all offers of help with wild anger."

The D.C. nodded his head, "I know Kibiriti. A strange man who will do damage and violence when in one of his fits of anger. But there is a way out. Could you be at Mpuguzi at two o'clock? I should not be surprised if you had a very sick patient to bring to hospital, named Mosi."

It was five minutes to two as we drove up the hill behind Mpuguzi. "Stop, Bwana," said Daudi. "From here we can see everything that happens."

Below us was a typical stretch of Tanganyika's Central Plains with its wide expanse of thornbush jungle broken by

millet gardens and low hills topped with granite boulders. In a grove of baobab trees were a number of houses, most of them of the sort that Stanley saw when he stood on this same hill nearly a century ago. There was one obvious modern touch in the wireless aerials which stuck up through many of the mud roofs.

The sound of flutes and drums drifted up to us from the centre of the village and every now and then the strange note of the *kudu* horn mingled with the noise of jostling, chattering people. They were giving the D.C. a musical welcome.

Suddenly, without warning, the crowd split open, and into the clearing strode a figure who seemed to have come out of the past. He was rubbed all over with red ochre. He started up a wild solo dance, but the drums fell silent. "Beat those drums!" he yelled. "Beat them! Beat them! BEAT THEM!"

He snatched a spear from a by-stander and brandished it excitedly. There was a struggle as two Askaris moved up to him, grasped his wrist and wrested the weapon from him. Daudi chuckled as the red-ochred figure was marched off along the path down which he had come.

"What now, Daudi?"

"Wait, Bwana."

The drums started their rhythm again. Five minutes later I saw one of the policemen trotting along the path towards us. In his hand was a note. I opened it and read:

"DEAR DOCTOR,

I noticed your car standing not far from the road. Would it be convenient to come into the village and pick up a very sick lad who should be in hospital? His father is a little irresponsible. The boy's name is Juma Mosi. I will be grateful for your co-operation.

Yours sincerely,
NELSON KOLONGO
District Commissioner."

I passed this over to Daudi. He grinned. "Bwana, you must do what the Government asks you in these matters."

I started the engine. The Askari climbed in next to Daudi and we drove down the hill. He pointed to a house on the out-skirts of the village. As we arrived a bed was carried out. On it lay a desperately sick boy. His knees and ankles were gnarled like the limbs of an oak tree. We lay him gently in the back of the Land Rover. Twice during that six-mile drive I thought he had stopped breathing. It was a great relief to see him safely in the corner bed.

"Would you check his blood, and type him, Daudi?"

My face grew longer and longer as I examined his heart, his liver, his spleen, his lungs. All of them were in trouble. He had two ulcers on his unbelievable legs.

I was making an effort to count his pulse when Daudi whispered over my shoulder, "His haemoglobin is 19%, Bwana; the lowest we've ever had in the hospital."

"That means only one thing, Daudi."

He nodded. "A transfusion. *Kah!* And he is one of the rare types. You remember how hard it was to find anyone to give blood for young Tembo. He's the same type. The only men we know who have compatible blood are on *safari* and we can't use Baruti's since that attack of fever." He shrugged. "We can go and type many people and try to find a donor, but it will take time."

"We'll have to do it fast, Daudi."

"But Bwana. . . ." Young Tembo had been standing behind me. "Why not take some of mine? I owe the hospital a pint."

Daudi chuckled. But I didn't like the idea. The boy was recovering from severe tuberculosis and needed every drop of blood to fight his own battles. I looked across at Mosi. His need was critical.

"Tembo, if we take any of your blood it will mean that you will have to lie quietly in bed for a whole week."

He nodded his head. "Did I not look like he looks when I first came in? And did not blood save me?"

"That's true, Tembo, and perhaps you'll be able to tell Mosi later on of the other great sickness you had and of the way in which Jesus helped you."

Daudi took the boy into a side room and I bent over Petro. The bed creaked as the sick man tossed irritably. The pain of movement shocked him back into consciousness for a few seconds, then his eyes closed again. It was a little soon to expect results from the penicillin, but I had hoped for more improvement than was being shown.

Daudi's voice called softly, "Bwana, would you come here

please?" He looked anxiously towards Tembo. "I've collected half a pint."

It was obvious that the plucky young donor could not give any more. "That will be a big help, Daudi. Give it as quickly as you can."

Tembo lay exhausted in bed, but there was a gleam in his eyes. "Bwana, is it working? Is my blood helping him?" Daudi had started the transfusion. Tembo's questions were answered as we watched death losing its grip on Mosi's life.

I whispered to Mali, "Keep the place quiet. This boy's going to need every scrap of medical and nursing skill that we have. He and Petro are two of the toughest problems we have had in the ward."

Unexpectedly the boy's eyes opened. He looked at Mali and then at me, and with fear welling up in his eyes he cried, "Where is my father?"

"All is well, Mosi. Lie quietly. This is the hospital. We've brought you here to help your sickness."

"Do the medicines of the hospital hurt?"

"Some complain that there is too much sugar in them."

Mosi gaped. "Sugar?"

"*Ngheeh*," said Tembo, "sugar. There are medicines that will bring joy to your stomach."

"But I want joy in my legs."

Baruti limped over and tapped his plaster-covered shin. "See that? The bone is broken inside so the Bwana put another sort of bone outside while the inside one heals."

"*Kah!*" gasped Mosi, "will they do that to me?"

I handed him a lump of brown sugar. "Try this for a start!"

CHAPTER III

THE BUG

THE ward report next morning read:

"*Mosi*: unconscious, but quiet. Bed in mess because of large lump of brown sugar given by Doctor.

Petro: restless night. Lost all medicines."

Daudi pointed to the nearly empty flask above Mosi's bed. "What now, Bwana?"

"Continue to run fluid into his veins. Keep it going for at least twenty-four hours. He's starved, and this is the only way to feed him for the moment. Also, run in a million units of penicillin, to deal with any stray germs that may have ideas."

An hour after sunset we again stood between the beds of our two dangerously ill patients. Mosi appeared to be asleep, and the apparatus above his bed was working well. I felt the boy's pulse and shook my head. "He's not picking up, Daudi. We can alter that with a pint of blood though. Will you find a suitable donor?"

"*Ndio*—yes," he called, as he hurried away.

The ward nurse showed me Petro's chart. "There's no improvement, Bwana. Not even a little."

"You're right. Give him another million units of penicillin. This infection of his is gaining strength."

Baruti beckoned to me. In a low voice he said, "Kibiriti is a man of hostility and of ugly temper. It will be a thing of wonder if he doesn't kill someone some day. Once he was only full of harsh words, but now he does violent things. Travel with your eyes open, Bwana."

"Better still, Baruti, prepare your weapons." I loaded a syringe with a powerful drug, and put it on a small tray beside his bed. "Look after this for me."

Baruti sniffed. "Has this strength against a spear or a stick in the hand of an angry man?"

"You'd be surprised, Baruti."

"Don't *you* be surprised, Bwana."

That evening I read the latest book on fungus diseases and then listened to the late news from the T.B.C. Then, turning off the radio, I went up to the hospital.

Something moved vaguely in the shadows, but I took no notice, thinking it was a hyæna. My mind was turning over and over again the facts of Petro's illness.

Mwendwa, the night nurse, said quietly, "He's worse. It is not easy now to give him fluids by mouth."

Petro's skin was burning hot. He grunted and opened his eyes, looked at me vaguely and muttered something about a *safari*. "Behold! His wisdom is on *safari*," said Mwendwa.

"Truly, Mwendwa. I can't risk keeping on with penicillin by itself. We'll give streptomycin as well."

She nodded. "We have none here, Doctor."

"I'll collect some from the dispensary."

I did, but only five small bottles came to light. We searched every ward and medicine cupboard, but found no more. Mwendwa reminded me that it took two weeks for supplies to come from Nairobi and we had enough for only two days.

Petro's infection was racing ahead; we could not ration the drug. Two ampoules had to be given at once.

As the nurse injected Petro sat bolt upright and shouted wildly. Mosi abruptly came back to consciousness. There was stark fear in his eyes. Mwendwa had her hands full looking after Petro. Baruti slipped out of bed and hobbled across to help me.

"Hold Mosi's arm. See the needle doesn't come out."

Tembo was also out of bed, gently holding the shoulders of the sick boy. He looked at me questioningly. I nodded. "Good boy, Tembo. Thank you. But go back to bed as soon as you can."

Baruti said quietly, "Mosi, there is no cause for fear. We are giving you medicines that will help you."

Hoarsely from the boy's throat came the words, "My father will have anger. . . ."

"He is not here," said Baruti. "All is well."

"*Eheh*," I agreed, injecting a sleeping medicine into the rubber tube which ran the fluid into the boy's arm.

"*Koh!*" said Tembo, "that's how I like to be given a needle. *Heeh*, it gives no pain when you inject that way." His knees started to wobble. Smiling, I picked him up and put him back to bed. "You can see why I said you need to lie quiet for five days."

I moved towards the door. "Mwendwa, call me if there's trouble tonight. I'll be here at sunrise."

She nodded. "*Kwaheri*, Bwana."

The dark walk to my house did not bring any bright ideas for helping Petro. Wearily I walked through my back door hardly realizing that it was wide open. Force of habit made me pick up an insecticide spray, then I saw that something very much larger than a mosquito was rummaging in a cupboard in my bedroom. Wide awake now I draped a grey blanket over the doorway and shouted, "*Nhawule!* What goes on?"

With a grunt of surprise a figure dashed past me and through the door. The blanket wrapped itself neatly around him, partly muffling his yell as he rolled over and over. I grabbed his arm and wrenched away the blanket.

A weasel-faced man peered at me, and when he had enough breath he pleaded in a whining voice, "Bwana, do not kill me! It is only I, Kuguni!"

"So you're Kuguni. What are you doing in my house?"

"Have pity on me, Bwana. There is sorrow in my stomach! There are many snakes within me that make much noise, and I said to myself, 'If only I could have the strong medicine that the Bwana uses for himself when his snakes hiss within him, then all will be well.'"

"There is no such medicine—if my stomach has no joy I take the white medicine of the hospital."

"Bwana, do not deceive me—the fame of that secret medicine, hot as flame, has gone far through the country."

Then I remembered the ginger essence tasted by one of our water carriers months before. "*Kah!* Kuguni, at last I understand you. There is some stuff here. It is not really medicine, but its taste is stronger than fire."

"Bwana, I will praise its strength."

"Very well. Promise also you will come to the hospital for treatment in future, and do what we tell you regarding medicines."

"I agree, Bwana."

I chuckled, went inside, and filled a tablespoon of ginger

concentrate and sampled a drop. "*Kah!* I would not have surprise if smoke came from within you."

"That's the medicine, Bwana." He clutched the spoon, swallowed the ginger at a gulp and stood breathless for a moment, then gripped my hand, and smote his stomach a tremendous blow.

"*Yoh!*" he gasped, "that's medicine, Bwana!"

He scuttled off into the night.

At 1 a.m. I was called in to see a sick baby. Penicillin was working in his case. On my way back I stopped at the men's ward. Mwendwa was bending over Petro, moistening his lips. "He's still delirious, Bwana."

"What about his blood slides, Mwendwa?"

"Daudi brought the report in soon after you went to bed. There's no malaria or tick fever."

"It's unlikely to be a tropical disease then. The ugly fact is that unless we stop this infection he will die. At 4 a.m. see that he has his second dose of streptomycin."

As we watched Petro broke out into a copious sweat. His teeth chattered and the bed seemed to shake. Mwendwa tried to give him a drink from a cup. He spilled a lot of it and started muttering, "I can't swim. The water will go over my head!" She shook up his pillows and laid him back quietly. Then she turned to me, "Bwana, you go and have some rest. They'll be wanting you at dawn and it's after two o'clock now."

On the dark path to my house I too started to sweat as I realised that we had enough streptomycin for only another twenty-four hours. I prayed silently for some answer to this problem.

Again weariness hit me and with it the vivid thought, "Why ask for the impossible? You're up against something that can't happen. This faith and trust in Almighty God is nothing but a pious hope."

I stopped in my tracks, recognizing where this line of argument came from. Under my breath I said, "Enough of that stuff, Satan; you'll have to do better than that. My faith IS in God." As I undressed and slipped under the mosquito net and sank into sleep the words, "God will supply all your need" echoed and re-echoed through my mind.

It was half light when Mboga's insistent voice called, "*Hodi*, Bwana. Wake up! *HODI!*"

I rubbed my eyes. "What's up, Mboga?"

"It's second cock-crow, Bwana. Mwendwa says that although Petro's asleep his leg looks bad. Also, I have news of Mosi's father...."

"*Ngoja*—hold on. I'll be with you in a moment."

As I dressed, Mboga played softly on his *ilimba*. I grinned at him. "Is your news as sad as your tune?"

"It is not a thing of joy, Bwana. Kibiriti is blazing with anger. He knocked down three Askaris and rushed in this direction through the thick thornbush."

"*Hongo!* We will keep our eyes open, Mboga."

We walked together to the hospital and into the ward. Mwendwa came over with her report. "Petro was delirious till an hour after the streptomycin injection, Bwana. After that he slept and his temperature is down two degrees, but his leg is more swollen."

"I'll look at that when he wakes. Sleep to him means life at the moment." I held up the last two ampoules of streptomycin. "If we had a dozen of these all would be well, Mwendwa, but when these two bottles are empty he'll only be at the beginning of the road back to life."

Daudi came through the door, "Bwana, I have tested Mosi's blood again. The haemoglobin is 42% now."

"That's better, but not good enough. We must transfuse him again."

Daudi nodded, "I have found one of the school-teachers who is the right type. The blood is already collected; I'll connect it up."

In five minutes the transfusion was going smoothly.

"*Hongo*," said Tembo, "that blood looks good. Is it stronger than mine? Perhaps it will help Mosi more."

"Your blood made all the difference when his need was greatest, Tembo. Eat strongly, and remember you must keep very quiet for five days."

I tiptoed past Petro's bed. He was still sound asleep. I bent over Mosi. "Is your arm hurting?" He shook his head, and then I caught a whisper, "Bwana, my father will come with anger."

"Don't have fear. We'll look after you. Close your eyes now and rest. Strength is coming into you. You'll feel better before the sun is overhead."

Daudi adjusted the flow of blood, running it in faster. He spoke in English. "It's like pouring water on sand with this boy. The transfusion is half way; he seems to absorb all we give and not show much result."

"He's a solid medical problem Daudi. There are many diseases clutching at his life. We have to fight each of them. But first we must build up his strength."

Daudi nodded. "*Eheh, fight* is the word, especially when his father arrives on the scene. And Bwana, he *will*. *Kumbe!* Within me my stomach quivers."

I picked up the syringe we had prepared the day before. "Keep this handy, Daudi. In it is a very powerful drug which will blunt the teeth of even the fiercest anger. They use it on wild animals—it makes a rhino as quiet as a cow. If Kibiriti comes, stick the needle in anywhere you can, and inject fast. Now for a little breakfast."

"Bwana, my eye feels sore," called an old man from the far end of the ward. I stood in the doorway. "I'll examine it Great One when . . ."

Something crashed into my shoulder. I cannoned into a table. Bowls and dishes clattered all over the floor. Mosi screamed in terror as a furious man waving a knobbed stick leaped towards the bed where he lay. Grunting with rage he smashed his stick into the transfusion apparatus. Broken glass and blood went all over the place. Daudi dived forward, grasping the rubber tube in his fingers. Baruti stumbled to his feet gripping a three-legged stool. "Drop that stick, Kibiriti!" he roared.

But Mosi's wild-eyed father sprang at Daudi, swinging his

murderous knobkerri. Baruti threw the stool. It caught Kibiriti in the pit of the stomach; he let out a groan and doubled up. I whipped up the syringe and plunged the needle into his shoulder muscles. Gasping, he turned on me, but Baruti pushed a pillow into his face with one hand and grabbed the stick with the other.

Mali appeared on the scene and very calmly began to sweep up the glass. "Stay where you are everybody, or we'll have cut feet and more work to do!"

Daudi removed the needle from Mosi's arm and was standing by his bed with his arm around the terrified boy, quietly guarding him. Kibiriti, struggling hard, was being held down by four men. "You'll kill him! You'll kill him!" he shrieked.

Mosi was shivering violently. "*Koh!*" muttered Daudi, "why does he do this?"

"I think it is sheer terror, Daudi, but are you sure no air went into his veins when the bottle was broken?"

"No, Bwana, I held the tube."

"Excellent work! If air finds its way into a person's veins it can cause clotting in the heart and death."

"*Ndio*," agreed Daudi, "but we are ahead of that trouble."

The man on the floor was still making a fight of it. I wondered that he was not making more noise until I saw the way Mboga was now using the pillow. "Good work, Baruti. Mboga, please don't choke him completely."

Solemnly Mboga panted, "I will follow your orders with care, Great One."

I concentrated on the sick boy. It took an uncomfortable half-hour to bring him back to normal. When at last we could relax I looked down the ward. Everything was quiet again. Nurses were counting pulses, taking temperatures and writing up charts. One was doing dressings for a number of eye cases and describing for them vividly all the things that had been happening. In the far corner of the ward a bed had been placed near the doorway. Four big men stood round it.

A weary-looking Daudi came towards me. "*Hongo*," he said, "if anyone asked me what is the news, I would reply, The news is good, but not very, for behold, the boy, Mosi, is unconscious; his father also is unconscious—which is a good thing; but I, *koh!* I am half dead!"

There was the sound of a long yawn. Petro stretched his

arms, leaned out of bed, picked up a cup of water and drank thirstily. I smiled at him. "That's the way, Petro. The more water you drink the better for you and the worse it is for your germs."

He yawned again. "*Yoh!* I had the strangest dream, Bwana. All sorts of things seemed to be happening."

Daudi rolled his eyes, "All sorts of things *seemed* to be happening! *Kah!* Behold that stuff stops pain with strength and brings sleep even more strongly. Surely this streptomycin is helping him greatly."

I moved close to him. "It certainly is, but we have one solid problem. There is only enough of it in the place to carry us beyond sundown."

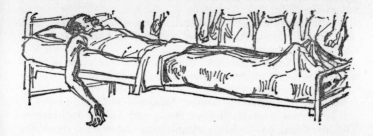

CHAPTER IV

THE PLANE

THE ward nurses stood around Kibiriti's bed. He lay quiet under the effects of the powerful tranquillizer.

"*Hongo!*" said Daudi, "if we had let him run wild he might have killed people. He is a man of anger."

I agreed. "Truly Daudi, though it is hard to believe that this is only temper. Something else, something very wrong must be happening in his head. While he's like this I will examine his eyes. Pass me the ophthalmoscope."

With the flick of a switch a small lamp came alive. I peered into Kibiriti's eyes and whistled softly. "There is evidence of a swelling inside his skull. Often people with this trouble have strong headaches and great sickness and behave strangely. Within Kibiriti's head is a growth—a very serious sickness indeed—a cancer. I have not the experience to operate on him, but there is someone who could. These days through the goodness of the East African Medical Research Council there is a doctor of special skill who flies from place to place in a small aeroplane ..."

"Could he not come here and operate on Kibiriti?"

"The trouble is, Mboga, that we have not the instruments which we would need. Kibiriti will have to go to Nairobi."

"He will die if he stays here?"

"I'm afraid so."

"Bwana," said Daudi, "this man of anger is waking up."

33

I injected a second dose of the calming medicine.

Baruti looked through the window, "*Hongo!* Bwana, we have visitors."

On the far side of the river bed, which two days before had been in full flood, skidded and slithered a Land Rover. It stopped under a baobab tree.

"*Heeh!*" laughed Mboga, "they are near the place of holes where you went swimming the other day, Bwana."

Tembo's voice came shrilly, "It's Bwana Kolongo!"

Soon we were shaking hands. "*Habari*—what's the news?"

"The news is good, Bwana D.C., and full of excitement. The boy Mosi has had two transfusions—or strictly speaking, one and a half. His father arrived in the middle of the second, swung a stick and created quite a bit of chaos."

The D.C.'s eyes twinkled. "And what did you do?"

"Gave him a drug that will keep him quiet for hours. This gave us a chance to examine him and find that he has a brain tumour. Now his only chance is for us to contact the doctor from the Medical Plane. With his help we might be able to save Kibiriti's life."

The D.C. nodded briskly. "Come over to my Land Rover."

In the back was an imposing box with an insulator and a long aerial. He threw a switch, picked up a microphone and said, "Nelson Kolongo calling Dodoma Central. Over."

A voice came back, "Dodoma Central, receiving you loud and clear. Go ahead Mr. Kolongo. Over."

"Have you news of Dr. Forrest? Over."

"Yes, Mr. Kolongo. We've been in touch with him a few minutes ago. I'll line things up and you can speak to him direct."

The District Commissioner smiled at me. "Communications of this sort used to take days. Now it's minutes. You really need an airstrip here suitable for light planes."

I nodded. "It would be a great help. But again we have the problem of communications."

The D.C. smiled broadly. "Not for long. The Research Foundation has a radio phone for you." He indicated the electronic equipment at his elbow. "Tomorrow the machine and the antennae will be installed . . ."

A voice came from the loud-speaker, "Forrest speaking. Over."

"Kolongo here, Dr. Forrest, I am at Mvumi. We have a man with a brain tumour. Will you speak to the doctor?"

He handed me the microphone. We discussed technical matters for a few moments. Then Dr. Forrest said, "I plan to fly back to Nairobi in an hour. Could you prepare an emergency landing-strip?"

I looked across at the District Commissioner. He nodded. "The local football ground and the gardens at each end."

I pressed the button on the microphone. "Dr. Forrest, Mr. Kolongo has this matter under control. We'll use the local football ground plus extensions. Over."

There was a crackle of static and then Dr. Forrest's voice, "Roger. Have the man ready to be picked up. This will have to be very much a flying visit. Over."

"Roger. It's very much in order, thank you. By the way, could you ask your Nairobi Base people to arrange for some streptomycin to be airmailed to me urgently. I have a man on the danger list who is responding to it, but we've only two ampoules left. Over."

His cheerful voice came through the loud-speaker, "Roger. Will order it for you, but I can do better than that. I have a dozen ampoules with me. I'll give them to you when I see you. Over and out."

Daudi looked at me and gripped my arm. Here was the complete answer to an impossible situation.

The next half-hour was tremendously busy. We prepared the sick man for his flight. Fifty schoolboys and a score of hospital people leapt to work. The goal-posts were wrenched out and thrown under a tree. The corn stalks from the gardens at the end of the football ground were pulled out, holes were filled in and stones rolled into the moist earth with a forty-four-gallon drum filled with sand.

Then came the sound of a small aircraft. It came in to land, and was soon surrounded by cheering people. Mosi's still unconscious father, transferred to a special stretcher, was placed in the back of the aircraft. The pilot was carefully examining the landing strip. "We used every foot of it," he remarked. "If you could extend it another hundred yards we could use this place regularly. Just as well we have a strong breeze today."

"*Kah!*" came an aggrieved voice, "what about my garden?"

"You shall have another one," answered the D.C.

"What about the work that I've done in it?"

"We will dig the other one for you with a tractor," smiled Mr. Kolongo.

The tall English doctor shook my hand. "We'll do what we can for this chap, and be in touch with you. By the way here is your streptomycin; expect me back before long." He climbed into the plane, calling "*Kwaheri*, good-bye," to the crowd, and in a moment they were off again.

"*Heeh!*" said Daudi, "here is another new big thing that has happened to us."

"It is!" agreed Nelson Kolongo, "and it is easier to travel up there than on our roads. I had a little trouble coming out. A dozen or so large granite boulders had rolled down from a hillside and completely blocked the road. Below them the river had cut a new channel ten feet deep. An impassable affair. We have a winch on the Land Rover so it was only half-an-hour's work to fill the wash-away with the boulders. Neat, I thought."

"Nimble thinking, Mr. Kolongo."

"*Hongo*," said Daudi slowly, "turning a block into a bridge."

He was telling Petro about this when I went up to the ward. "Sickness is like that, Petro, it can be a block if you let it stay like that."

Petro turned over the pages of his rather worn Bible and read, "When all kinds of trials and temptations crowd into your life, don't resent them as intruders, but welcome them as friends."

CHAPTER V

RADIO PHONE

Kᴜɢᴜɴɪ pressed his face against the mosquito wire and leered through the window. "Petro, the news is good. Hewa is now at Miti's house. She will hear that they took one man of anger away from here and left the other behind. . . ."

Mboga grasped an insecticide spray, bent double, came to the window and pumped a cloud of pungent fumes into

Kuguni's face. "Clear out, Insect!" he roared. He raced through the door brandishing his weapon, but Kuguni had scuttled off.

Mwendwa brought me the report. I read through it, and stopped at Petro's name. "At 8 p.m. you gave streptomycin?"

Mwendwa nodded. "The last dose we had in the place." She looked at me anxiously. "What are we going to do now?" As I produced the new packet of the antibiotic, her eyes opened wide. "Where did you find those, Bwana?"

"They came from the sky, Mwendwa. I'm going to tell Petro about it now."

Petro lay in bed moodily watching the shadow of the night nurse on the opposite wall. I sat down beside his bed. "*Habari?*"

He sighed heavily. "The news is good, Bwana." He winced

as he moved his legs impatiently under the blanket. "But . . . you heard the words of Kuguni?"

"Yes, I heard his words."

"*Kah*, because of my anger I've ruined everything. Hewa has gone to Miti's house—the worst possible place for her to be, and it's all because of my anger."

"Why don't you write her a letter and tell her you've made a mistake, and ask her to come here and see you?"

"*Kah!* She wouldn't come."

"My prayer has been that she would. Do you think when she comes forty miles closer to you that she is farther away?"

He lay there silent. I went on. "Petro, something happened today which has put new muscles into my faith. These days you have had throbbings in your legs. Mine were inside my mind. You see I have a friend who was very ill, but my mind was at rest for I had pink capsules that would cure his fever. But his stomach had no joy in those pink capsules. My mind smiled wisely and told me, 'Inject penicillin; that will give his stomach no work in the matter;' so penicillin was injected; but it lacked strength to deal with the trouble. He grew worse rapidly and his life was in danger. My mind told me, 'Do not sweat, keep calm, there is still streptomycin to inject. This will work,' and it did."

Petro smiled, "It did indeed, and I am thankful."

"Wait! What you didn't know—but my mind did, and that was the reason for its throbbing—was that we had only three doses of streptomycin left. The one you were given at sunset was the last. And we still need to give streptomycin for many days."

Petro's mouth fell open. "Is there no more?"

"There's not another drop of it in the dispensary. Orders were sent, but it has to come from Nairobi."

"*Kah!* Then perhaps a week will pass before more arrives— perhaps even two weeks. What shall we do?"

I stood beside him. "Please Petro, stop talking like my mind. It's been asking these questions for two days, and much of two nights. The only way to have a mind at peace is to tell God all about your problem—to pray."

"But how could God help us with this? Can he send us medicine from heaven?"

"That's exactly what He did, Petro. Look!" I produced

the box of streptomycin. "Here are twelve doses. They were flown to Mvumi in the first aeroplane ever to land in the village, and because of this medicine the disease that threatened your life will have its teeth drawn. God hasn't forgotten you, Petro. He hasn't forgotten Hewa, or Aramu."

"*Hongo!*" said Mwendwa, "truly this medicine did come from the sky."

Petro was sitting up, his face glowing. "Bwana, do not put the lamp out for a moment. I will write to Hewa."

He chewed the stub of a pencil, and every now and then wrote something. At last he shook his head. "*Yoh!* Bwana, the words will not come."

"Go to sleep then, and you will find that tomorrow morning they will come through your mind like water through a pipe."

At nine o'clock the next morning I walked into the ward. Mali smiled up at me. "Bwana, for once the news IS good. The temperature of each of them is 99°."

"Thanks, Mali. That is very good news. *Habari*, Petro?"

He smiled, "Bwana, the news is GOOD. *Kumbe!* sleep escaped me *kabisa* till second cock-crow. But this was a good thing, for I wrote my letter in the dark—the writing wobbles, but the words were right." He dropped his voice to a whisper. "Mosi also lay there without sleep, and when he saw I was awake too, he said, 'Bwana Petro, do you know if God goes to sleep at night and forgets about people?'"

"I told him that the Bible says God does not sleep, and that His eyes are always watching us." He said, 'Does God watch us to make sure we only do right things?' I told him that the Good Shepherd watches us because He loves us, not because He wants to pry or punish. Then he said, 'I wish I was one of God's sheep and that He looked after me.' I told him it was not difficult to come into God's family, or to become a member of His flock, and he asked me how.

"I said, 'If someone came to your house what would he say?'

"'*Hodi?* May I come in?'

"'And you would reply?'

"'*Karibu*—come in. But only if I wanted him to.'

"'That's how it is with the Lord Jesus. Tembo and Baruti and the Bwana and I believe that He came into our hearts to live there for ever because we said, "*Karibu*—come in." He won't push open the door, Mosi; we must ask Him in. When you do this you become one of His sheep and He is your shepherd.'"

He looked at the sleeping boy. "I think he understands."

Mosi opened his eyes as Tembo shouted, "It's coming—the bird with the engine!" He stopped, then burst out, "Bwana, I can walk about today, can't I? My blood is good, isn't it?"

"Sorry, Tembo, it's bed for you—your legs still wobble. Stay close to Mosi today."

His face dropped, but he nodded.

High above us the small plane circled as Daudi and I joined the streams of people hurrying down towards the football field.

"Listen, everybody!" called Daudi, "you must stand well back whenever the aeroplane is alive, and when the engine is going—there is danger in that whirling thing that is called a propeller—it hits harder than the trunks of six elephants."

We indicated the direction of the wind. The pilot gunned his engine, circled and made a perfect landing. He opened the door of the aircraft and stepped down, waving to the crowd. "I came to see your man, Petro," he said, gripping my hand, "and I thought you should have more streptomycin. By the way, Nelson Kolongo is bringing out a rehabilitation expert and one of his trainees, the blind mechanic who will put in your radio phone." He turned towards the plane, "Mr. Fungo!"

A most competent-looking man stepped somewhat hesitantly from the aircraft and held out his hand a little vaguely. Dr. Forrest smiled. "Mr. Fungo's eyes are in his fingers. He's one of the first trained communications officers. He's totally blind but that doesn't interfere with his job in the least."

I shook hands with Mr. Fungo, and Dr. Forrest went on, "Have you anything else you'd like me to do while I'm here?"

"Will you tackle two jobs? Would you have a word with young Mosi, whose father went with you to Nairobi, and will you operate on a surgical emergency that has just come in?"

"I'll operate gladly," said the surgeon, "But I wonder whether I should tell Mosi how ill his father is. Samuel Mabarti, the rehabilitation man, would do it much better."

Daudi took Dr. Forrest to the operating theatre while I talked to Mr. Fungo about the radio telephone. The electronics man very quickly sized up the situation. He deftly handled his instruments and said, "This office is a very suitable spot, Doctor. We ought to have the machine in action by the later afternoon if we can put the antenna up by then."

Mali came hurrying towards me. "Doctor! Twins! Hurry!"

Mr. Fungo laughed, "I'm glad it's your job and not mine."

I called at the door of the operating theatre, "Urgent call to the arrivals end of the hospital—two at once."

"Carry on," smiled the surgeon. "I'll go ahead here with Daudi."

We had a more than busy hour, and the smaller twin was not breathing well, when the nurse whispered, "Mboga is at the window, Doctor, with a message."

"Speak up, Mboga!"

"Bwana Kolongo is here with a large lorry full of great posts, a large box and much wire. With them is a man. They say his feet are cold, that there is no blood supply to his legs, and that you cannot feel the arteries anywhere from the knees down."

"That's nasty, Mboga. Put him in the examination room. Raise the end of the bed, feet higher than head. Hot water bottles, blankets, whole anti-shock routine—but don't burn him."

There was a queer twist around Mboga's lips as he said, "Bwana, I certainly will not burn these legs."

"You can't be too careful; legs like his are terribly easy to damage."

At that moment the baby started to cry lustily.

In came Dr. Forrest: "How are you going?"

"All's well here now, but a new problem has arrived—a man with something radically wrong with his legs."

"Did he come with Nelson Kolongo?"

"I believe he did. Care to come and have a look?"

Again that queer half-smile appeared—this time at the corners of Dr. Forrest's lips.

Lying in the examination room was a tall, good looking African, his legs covered with blankets. He raised himself on one elbow, and sipped a steaming cup of sweetened tea. Seeing me, he greeted, "*Habari*, Bwana?"

"My news is good, but what of your legs? Have you pain, or numbness, or cramps?"

A slow smile spread over his face. "I would be most grateful if you would examine me."

Daudi was already taking off the blankets. The people standing round the doorway grinned and chuckled. I said rather sternly, "This is nothing to laugh at. The man has trouble with his legs which could be very serious indeed. Is there any joke in this thing?"

From behind me came a roar of laughter. Baruti was enjoying himself hugely, "*Eheh*, Bwana—behold, there is much food for amusement. There is a big joke! Look!"

Our patient was sitting with his legs dangling over the side of the table. There was no doubt that they were cold, pulseless and bloodless—they were made of aluminium! I looked in amazement, and then joined in the laughter. "*Yoh!* Many people have been pulling my legs with strength."

Dr. Forrest smiled, "Let me introduce you to Mr. Samuel Mabarti, the rehabilitation man." We shook hands.

"Where did you come by those legs, Mr. Mabarti?"

"I had a motor accident in England: both my legs were crushed when a lorry overturned. A friend of Dr. Forrest's amputated and afterwards helped me to buy these legs." He paused, "When anyone has travelled this particular road it is much easier to help others with the same problems, and so I studied rehabilitation. My job is to show men who feel hopeless that their fears have no strength."

I glanced towards the ward where Petro lay. "Your coming can have a very special usefulness. In the men's ward is one of our hospital staff—Dr. Forrest is going to examine him in a minute—and the fact that you are here could take the sting out of a very grim verdict on his legs."

"Shall we go and see him now?" asked Dr. Forrest. "By the way, while you were coping with the twins I had a look at the boy Mosi. He has a most difficult set-up. Both legs—mis-shapen to start with—have been broken in a number of places. They've healed all right, but in the most fantastic twisted 'Z' shape. Still, I think ultimately we can give him useful legs. Now for your man with the Madura foot."

As Mwendwa uncovered Petro's legs the surgeon sat down at the bedside and smiled, "Tell me your story."

"It was seven years ago, Doctor," said Petro. "One day

my foot was sore. I looked at my toe, and there was a *funza*. I dug it out with a safety pin."

There was a nodding of heads. Everybody knew only too well the minute ground flea which burrowed under the skin of people's toes, laying its eggs in a sac which looked like a grain of wheat.

Petro went on, "The toe did not heal; my foot swelled; lumps grew upon it, and then, *heeh!*—there was sorrow in my heart, for I saw other lumps appear, rough like the skin of a pineapple. To put my weight on my feet was a thing of pain, and later I could not even walk. So I came here. . . ."

Dr. Forrest looked across at me.

"We had him here for a long time. At the beginning I thought we'd have to amputate. But Petro is a man of great faith. We used all the available remedies, and slowly, with God's help he got back on to his feet. After that he was in charge of the Men's Ward for years, and last dry season we sent him to a branch hospital to relieve for twelve months."

The surgeon looked at me, "When he was in hospital years ago you told him that amputation was necessary?"

"I did."

"And he's been able to battle along ever since. It's a remarkable story."

"The whole business was remarkable then, but now the trouble has flared up again."

Dr. Forrest nodded and set to work examining Petro minutely. Then he stood up, walked to the window and drummed on the sill with his fingers. "I don't like it at all. It's been there too long. I have the feeling that this disease could have spread above his knees and his thighs. If it is beyond that we can do nothing. Let's remove a groin gland from each side; if they don't show any of the fungus we can safely operate. Shall I explain this to him?"

I nodded. In fluent Swahili he said, "Bwana Petro, I'm going to remove a gland from each side—up here—" he ran his finger along Petro's groin.

"Then my feet will have to go?"

Dr. Forrest spoke quietly, "Let's see how far the trouble has gone and then we'll know how big the operation needs to be."

Petro watched preparations for the minor operation with troubled eyes. Dr. Forrest noted this. He went to the door and

called out, "Samuel, please come in here for a moment."
Then he turned to Petro, "We can do some interesting things
these days. Through what is called rehabilitation people can
be taught to live normally again after they have had great in-
juries or serious operations. I want you to meet a friend of
mine who had a very severe accident. He has not only been
rehabilitated, but he has been trained to help others in the
same way. Bwana Sam, walk up and down the ward, and you,
Bwana Petro, see if you can tell me which of his legs is artificial."

"*Koh!*" said Petro, "but he has shoes on his feet."

"That is so," agreed Dr. Forrest. "They are very good,
these artificial limbs."

Through my mind went the thought, "And very expensive."

Petro watched every step that the tall African took as he
walked to the end of the ward and came back. "I would say
that the left leg is the artificial one, and that there is some
damage to his right knee."

Daudi brought a stool. Samuel Mabarti sat on it and
rolled up his left trouser leg. Petro's face broke into a smile,
"*Yoh!* I was right!" Then his eyes opened very wide as the
other trouser leg was slowly rolled up. Quietly Samuel
Mabarti said, "So you can see what can be done. But it takes a
while to learn to use them."

"*Hongo!*" said Petro, and there was a new gleam in his eye.

A voice came from outside. "The radio phone is working!
There's a message for Dr. Forrest."

People crowded round the door as Dr. Forrest picked up the
microphone. "This is Mvumi Hospital coming on to the air for
the first time! Mvumi Hospital calling Nairobi Central;
over."

From the speaker came a voice, "Nairobi Central, receiving you loud and clear. We have an urgent call for Dr. Forrest. Would you bring him to the microphone. Over."

A few minutes later Dr. Forrest put the microphone back into its place and said, "I'll remove those glands and then it's a matter of flying back post haste to Nairobi."

CHAPTER VI

DOLLA

A LOUD sneering voice came from the ward.

"*Koh!*" said Daudi, "that's Dolla, who brought the radio phone. He's Hewa's brother, and a man of noise and nastiness."

The rasping voice went on, "Who has money and a job, you or I? Who has clothes and a gramophone and a radio, who I say? Not you, Petro Chilango, but I, Dolla Nhoto." He spat. "Why your wife hasn't even shoes, and you—if you had shoes yourself—what use could you make of them?"

"Move out of here, Loud-mouth!" said Baruti.

Dolla swung round, "Shut-up, you seller of mouldy skins. You're finished. These days it's the men with money who go places in Africa. *Kah!*" he sneered, "I've heard you say that the Light of the World is Jesus, but I'm telling you that the light of the world is the shilling." He pushed his way through the door, slammed it, stepped into the lorry, tooted the horn loudly, drove deliberately over an ornamental tree and away.

Petro was shaking with anger. Mr. Mabarti spoke evenly, "Take it quietly. The laughter of hyæna comes loudly to the ear, but few have joy in hyænas, like Dolla."

Mosi was sitting up in bed. His voice came huskily. "Great One, my father was a man of anger."

Samuel Mabarti nodded. "I met him in Nairobi. I flew from there this morning."

"*Hongo*," said the child, "have you news then?"

"I bear news that is both good and bad, Mosi."

The boy whispered, "*Hongo!* What is it?"

"The body of Kibiriti, your father, is dead." Samuel bent over the sick boy. "But he heard the words of God, Mosi, at first with anger, but later with ears that listened. When he made the great *safari*, the disease of his soul was cured, and he lives now in the country of God."

There was a look of wonder on Mosi's face. "Bwana Petro, then the prayers that we prayed have been heard by God, and He has answered."

He lay back on his pillow and was soon asleep.

It was mid-afternoon next day. Petro lay on his bed with a drawn look on his face. He forced himself to smile. "Bwana, give me a large knobbed stick."

I raised my eyebrows, "What for, Petro?"

"To kill some rats that gnaw with strength."

"Let me take your pulse."

He grinned. "I'm not drunk. I'm not delirious. Neither of us can see these rats, but I can feel them. *Kumbe*, within my feet there is pain of the sort that gnaws and gnaws and gnaws."

"*Kah!* Petro, here is exactly the stick you need."

From the cupboard I took a bottle of pink pills. "Whenever the rats bite you, hit them with one of these. You hit hardest by swallowing with a large drink of water."

Petro smiled. "*Assante*, Bwana. Thank you."

Tembo touched my arm as I walked through the door. "Bwana, speaking of rats, is it true that you pay money for those caught near the hospital?"

"It is, Tembo; they are creatures of dirt and disease. I pay five cents for little ones, and ten cents for big."

"*Yoh!*" he chuckled, "it is a thing of joy. I shall ask Baruti to help me to make traps." He ran off as I stopped to listen to the music of a guitar. Baruti was keeping time with his big toe.

Seeing me the musician stopped, stood to attention, and said, "Bwana Doctor, I have a letter for you from the District Commissioner." He held up an envelope. "Also, I have brought a man to fix the concrete of the aerial of the new machine. He is staying with his relations." He pointed in the direction of Miti's house.

"*Koh!*" said Baruti, "that man Dolla again."

I thanked the driver and said, "Will you not taste the tea of the hospital and continue to bring food to our ears with your guitar while I read this letter?"

I went into the office with Daudi and Samuel Mabarti, tore open the envelope and read, "Pathology Report on tissue of Petro Chilango."

Daudi drew in his breath sharply. "What is the news, doctor?"

"The report is good. We shall be able to operate above the knee both sides."

Samuel Mabarti walked to the door. "Then we must work fast to obtain the new legs. I shall do all I can. The best way to start things going is at Dodoma, then at Nairobi."

I agreed, "But remember that this is a double problem—we need not only legs, but the money to buy them."

I read those fateful typewritten words of the report again, then picked up my pen and wrote,

"DEAR GEORGE,

I've told you about Petro in my circular letters. He is in acute need. Please pass this letter round in the right quarters.

I have before me a Pathology Report which reads,

Specimen I, from knees right and left: positive;

Specimen II, from right groin glands: negative;

Specimen III, from left groin glands: negative.

This may sound dull and technical, but it is packed with possibilities. If the reports on II and III had been positive, it would have meant crippledom, pain and death to Petro. But they are negative. We can save his life by amputating both legs above the knee. Modern type artificial legs can give him back full usefulness.

Put yourself in this man's place. If you faced double amputation, how would you feel? The legs he needs will cost new £100 or $300. The price of a holiday can open a new chapter of valuable living for a first-rate Christian chap. We have no emergency funds for this sort of thing. We need help urgently. Over to you."

I addressed the envelope to a friend in the home country, wrote a letter of thanks to Mr. Kolongo and handed them to the driver. Samuel Mabarti was sitting in the jeep. "*Kwaheri*," he called as they drove away.

Back in the ward we sat beside Petro's bed. I pulled out the envelope. "One large door has opened, Petro. The disease has spread to the knees, but not above. The operation can be done."

A little twisted smile came round his lips. "It is not easy to have joy when you hear that your legs can be cut off above the knees, Bwana.''

Daudi nodded slowly, ''Truly, but it's better to lose your legs than your life.''

''*Eheh*,'' agreed Petro. He looked down at his feet. ''I have prayed for years that God would cure me if that was His plan.'' He sighed. ''It seems that His answer is No, but I don't understand why.'' He shook his head, and looked again at his feet. ''When these go, what will I put in their place?''

''Did you see the legs that Bwana Samuel was wearing?''

''I saw them—but how can I buy legs like those? I have the hundred shillings I left with Hewa, perhaps that will be enough to buy one or two toes, no more.''

I broke in, ''These legs are a need, Petro, and the Bible says, 'My God shall supply all your needs according to His riches'. We must ask Him to supply. Money is one of the smaller things.''

Together we prayed and asked God to help us in this matter and in every step that lay ahead.

Mboga came running in. ''Bwana, a snake has spat in the eye of Mele the milkman!''

When I had dealt with this, Petro was frowning at a page full of figures. ''Bwana, if I put aside all my wages without spending one cent, it will take years to pay for those legs. Time and again you've told me that God opens doors to guide us and shuts doors if it is not the way to travel. Truly, one door seems to be open, but directly beyond it is another, and it's locked! *It's locked!*''

''There is a way of unlocking that door, Petro. Faith in God is the key. Talk to Him. Tell Him your need, and keep on telling Him. Do you believe that God will do what He promises?''

''I do, but I can't see how He's going to do it.''

''If you have faith in Him, that isn't necessary.'' I beckoned to Baruti and gave him some special instructions, and went outside. ''Watch this, everybody, and see if it helps you to understand about faith in God.'' I produced two equal lengths of strong rope, put one end of each in Petro's hand and the other through the window opposite him across the ward. ''These are to help you to sit up in bed. The name of each rope is FAITH, but there's a difference between them. Pull the first one.''

He did and it slipped through the window and flopped to the floor. "That one didn't help you much."

Petro shook his head.

"Now try the other." He pulled. It tightened. He sat up, then slowly and certainly he moved, bed and all, to the middle of the ward.

"*Koh*," laughed Tembo, "someone of strength is at the other end of that rope."

Baruti's grinning face appeared at the window.

"This is the answer. Both ropes are called faith. But understand this, faith by itself is of little use; but faith in God has solid strength to hold and help us. If we hang on firmly to our end of the rope, He is infinitely strong at His end. Think this over, especially you, Petro, as you go to sleep tonight."

In the morning, Petro was humming cheerfully to himself. "Bwana, I've been thinking of your two ropes, and of the doors that are open for me already. They are many. I am praying that God will open the others that are ahead of me."

"Excellent, Petro. But remember that no door opens unless you turn the knob. If you do this and give the door a little push and it still doesn't open, look for another door. Never kick the door open, or use a crowbar to force it open."

That day there were storms about, and Petro's feet were particularly sore. In the evening I could see he was feeling down. He sighed. "Two thousand shillings is an awful lot of money, Bwana."

"To us, yes, but not to God. Already I have written to friends in my home country."

Petro nodded, but I could see disappointment written deeply on his face.

There was a commotion at the door. "Not in my ward!" said Mali firmly.

"But you've got to!" said Tembo, "They're the Bwana's!" He scampered to my side clutching a number of dead rats by their tails.

"Ugh," said Mali, "take them outside."

Tembo stood his ground. "I caught them for the Bwana. There are seven large ones and five small."

I viewed the rodents carefully. "I should think they are worth a shilling, Mali."

"Truly," she smiled, "but outside—not in here."

Tembo gleefully took the shilling I held out to him, then he went and placed it in Petro's hand. "Bwana Petro, here is the first money for your legs. I thought of this way of helping when you talked about the rats that gnaw inside your feet." Then he turned to me. "Do you *want* these, Bwana, or may I roast them for Mosi and myself?"

I grinned. "You may have them, Tembo—all of them."

Petro's face was glowing. "Tembo, you've brought joy into a place that was dark with doubt."

Next morning Daudi took me aside. "Bwana, we can't count on that money Petro left with Hewa. I heard her brother Dolla boasting that he'd taken every shilling of it."

"That must be the reason why Petro's heard no word from her. She fears to tell him the money has gone. But why did she give it to him, Daudi?"

He shrugged. "This Dolla is a man of cunning."

Outside, Dolla was mixing cement, singing as he did so. I didn't catch the words, but Mali did. Indignantly she went to the window and called, "Stop that evil song!"

Dolla spat and went on singing. He tipped some water into the dust, scooped up a handful of mud and flung it through the hospital window. Mali and a junior nurse each grabbed a broom and hurried outside bent on revenge. I was just in time to prevent battle. Dolla threw another handful of mud. "Cut that out Dolla!"

"*Yoh!*" said Mali, "he shall scrub the ward where he threw that dirt."

"Shut up, you," jeered Dolla.

He picked up a shovel and came aggressively at me. "Look out, Bwana, he'll cut you in two!" yelled Mboga.

I stood my ground. "Put that down, Dolla."

He swung the shovel. Baruti moved in behind him and prodded him hard with the business end of a spear. "Drop it, or this spear will bite into your thigh."

Dolla stepped sideways, and tripped over a bucket. Out of his pocket dropped a roll of notes. Baruti calmly picked these up and said, "Bwana, I'll clean up the ward. Let him carry on with his work."

"Give me back that money!" shouted Dolla.

"It's not yours, it's Petro's."

"Hewa gave it to me to look after for her."

"We can help her in this matter better than you. She will tell us later what is to be done with the money."

Dolla was fuming, but when he saw the set of Baruti's jaw, he picked up the shovel and went on mixing cement.

Baruti whispered urgently, "We must keep him away from Petro at all costs, Bwana."

All that day he sat by the door playing his ilimba. As I passed I heard his voice, "I'm watching everything he does, Bwana. He is a man of danger. He will direct his anger and resentment against Petro, but my eyes will be open at all times."

We were all relieved to see the aerial in place and Dolla stalking off in the direction of Miti's house.

The bus passed him as it came up the hill. Gideon pulled up at the hospital and brought in the mailbag.

"*Hongo!*" said Petro, as I opened letter after letter, "it will take weeks, long weeks, for your letter to reach your friends; and for them to think and write, more weeks."

I had opened an envelope. Inside was a short and very much to the point note, "I have been in hospital two weeks. They have saved my life and taken away pain that has been severe for months. I am very thankful. I have thanked the surgeon and the hospital people here. I would like to thank God in a way that is more than words. Enclosed is five pounds. You will know how to use it."

I translated this for Petro's benefit. His eyes grew wide. "*Koh!* Bwana, and the words of God are, 'Before they call, I will answer.' He has!" He looked at the pile of empty envelopes. "I have a hundred shillings put aside, then there is Tembo's shilling, and this hundred. *Yoh!* We have started well."

Baruti shook his head. "I have news. Much has happened to those hundred shillings of yours. Hewa paid them to Dolla for charms and medicines to keep herself and Aramu from being damaged by spells. Dolla has a clever tongue, and Hewa's mind is not clear on these things." Baruti grinned widely, "But there is some joy in the situation. Today we recovered fifty shillings of the money. It fell from Dolla's pocket."

"*Koh!*" said Petro. "That's something. But, poor Hewa, if only I could walk again and help her."

CHAPTER VII

HARSH COUGH

Hewa stood in the doorway. The small boy beside her coughed in a way that shook his frail body.

"*Karibu*, come in Hewa." I brought her a chair and a stool for the boy. "What's the news?"

"Good, Bwana." She sighed, "But our troubles are many."

"What is your news, Aramu?"

"Good, Bwana, but I would have joy to see my father's face."

The last time I had seen Hewa she had been trimly dressed. Today she was barefooted and wearing the cheapest of black cloths. She put her head in her hands. "Bwana, what's to become of us?"

Around her neck was a charm; others dangled on the boy's painfully thin ankles. She drew her son close to her. "The child is ill; we have no food, no money. Nothing."

"*Hongo!* Hewa. Petro spoke of a hundred shillings that he left with you."

She shrugged.

Mwendwa was passing. "Please take Aramu to see his father." The boy took her hand and they went towards the ward.

"Have you seen Dolla lately, Hewa?"

Startled, she looked up at me. "Dolla?"

"Yes, your brother. Did you not give the hundred shillings to him to buy native medicines and charms?"

Her lips were framed to deny this, then she slumped back in the chair. "I had fear, Bwana. The sort of fear that *you* cannot understand."

I nodded. "But you gave him the money, Hewa?"

"*Eheh*. I gave him the money."

"Did you know that he kept half of it for himself?"

She sat bolt upright. "*Koh!* He didn't."

"Yes, he did. And we have it here."

"*Hongo!* What will Petro say?"

"Why not go and talk with him?"

She looked away. "Bwana, is his sickness very great?"

"It is, Hewa. His feet are so bad that they must be removed."

She stared at me. "Then this is the end! What's to become of us?" She wrung her hands.

"No, Hewa, all can be well. These days metal legs can be bought that fit so well that he will work again without difficulty. Come and talk with him."

Reluctantly she followed me into the ward. Petro's face beamed as she walked slowly towards his bed. He spoke in a low voice, but she seemed to take no notice. She did not come close, and her wide staring eyes seemed to look right through him. Then she pulled a corner of the black cloth over her face and slumped down on the floor.

"Hewa, forgive me for my anger." She gave no sign of hearing him; her voice came in a sing-song dirge: "They will cut off your feet, cut them off, and we will have famine in our house. . . ."

"No," said Petro, "that will not happen. Don't you understand, God will . . ."

Hewa struggled to her feet. Aramu shivered and shrank back from her. "God? *God?* What has He done for us?" She burst into tears and grasping her small son by the arm she dragged him from the ward into the half darkness.

Mboga called me, "Bwana, the radio telephone rings!"

I ran to the office. There was a lot of static. "Storms about, Daudi."

"*Eheh*," he agreed, "more than one sort! This visit of Hewa's has not helped, not even a little."

Abruptly from the machine came a voice. "Nairobi Base calling Mvumi Hospital. Are you receiving me? Over."

"Mvumi Hospital. Receiving you loud and clear. Over."

Then Dr. Forrest's voice came through the speaker, "Hullo, Mvumi. Sorry to report my hand is infected. I won't be with you for at least a month. Surgically I'm out of the firing line. What progress have you made with those people with troublesome legs? Over."

"Mosi, the boy with the twisted legs is slowly improving. Petro is much the same. His feet still give him misery. Over."

I was barely able to sort out the surgeon's voice from the crackle of static. "I haven't forgotten him. There is no chance of any support for his mechanical legs at this end. However, Mabarti is prowling round and seems to be on to something. Why don't you operate on the boy yourself; make it a three stage affair. I must go. Be in touch with you this day next week. Call me if anything new happens. *Kwaheri*. Over and out."

I turned the set off and looked at Daudi. "I'm going to see Petro now, Daudi."

We bent over his bed. "Another door shut, Petro. Dr. Forrest cannot operate for a month. He said there is no news of legs so far—or money to buy them."

"*Heeh!* Bwana. Let me also say that my news is good." And then in almost a whisper, "But, but, but, but."

I ran my fingers down his shinbone. "The pain?"

He nodded. "Truly! But I have also a deep ache in my heart. For many days it was there because no word came from Hewa, but today you saw and you heard."

I nodded.

"Bwana, did you see my child? He's very sick."

"*Eheh!* And so is your wife. She's sick with fear."

Petro nodded. "The trouble is, Bwana, she has small faith in God. Deep within her is faith in the old ways, in magic, in spells, and the fear of witchcraft grips her and she doesn't know what to do. I know what needs to be done. But there is no way to do it."

I sat down and leaned back in the chair. "Behold! God is asleep?"

He looked at me with astonishment.

"I didn't say that, Petro. I am only quoting Miti."

"*Kah!*" said Petro sitting up. "I see it. You have opened my mind with these words. I have the answer, God's own answer." From under his pillow he pulled his Bible. He flicked over the pages and read, "The Lord is your keeper" and "He that keeps you will not slumber." He smiled. "This is what I keep telling Mosi."

"Read on, Petro. See, it says, 'He will keep your going out and your coming in from this day and for ever.'"

Petro smiled, "*Heeh!* I have wasted much time with fears. Faith in God is better."

Baruti followed me out into the warm African night. "Bwana, you wanted me?"

"*Neheeh!* Baruti, you hunt animals with skill. You move through shadows and are not noticed."

"*Eheh*, but this plaster of mine makes me move slowly."

"We'll take it off now. Use your spear to lean on if the leg feels tired, but I would like you to keep close to Hewa and see what happens. The moon is large tonight."

"I will do this. And Bwana, when you remove this old friend from my leg, do it carefully. I will keep it to remind me of the strong bone outside my skin which helped me when my own bones had not enough strength. When others notice it and speak of it, I shall tell them what Jesus does to strengthen our weakness."

A few minutes later I watched him as he moved out into the shadows and seemed to disappear. His voice came softly, "Bwana, I am even now on my way."

Baruti went straight towards the place where Miti's house seemed to crouch in the gloom. He moved from shadow to shadow soundlessly. When he was within view of the house he saw Hewa and Aramu trudging along the road below. They turned off and stood outside Miti's door. Hewa looked anxiously this way and that and then called, "*Hodi?*"

Through the door stalked a tall figure. He stood looking beyond Hewa and then squatted down on his heels. Baruti could see his lips moving, but no sound reached him. He moved closer, and Hewa's voice came, "They will cut off his legs. They say that others of iron will be made for him, and that he will walk successfully with these."

Miti laughed harshly. "Words of no wisdom."

The moon was well up. Baruti watched the medicine man pick up a pair of cowhide sandals. He moved like someone in an hypnotic trance to a patch of moonlight. "The spirits shall tell us of this matter," he said, spitting on the sandals, and throwing them briskly on to the ground. Hewa stood well back. Baruti could see her trembling all over. Three times Miti threw the shoes, then he rocked to and fro and said in a toneless voice, "He will die. Petro will die."

Huddled on the ground, Aramu shivered violently. His eyes hooded and then he started to sing in a queer shrill voice. Miti grabbed Hewa by the shoulder, "Clear out and take him with you."

Hewa picked the boy up and ran wildly down the hill the way she had come. On and on she went until at last exhausted she stumbled to her knees under a thornbush. She gasped, "Oh, my mother, what shall I do?"

Aramu cried, "Look, my mother, look ahead of us!"

Moving towards them with its strange stilted gait was a chameleon, stark white and ghostly. Hewa screamed, picked up the boy and regardless of thorns dashed off at right angles to the path they had travelled. She came to a dry river bed and almost collapsed into the deep shadow of a mango tree. Suddenly she started to pray, "Oh God, oh God, what shall I do?"

A deep voice replied, "I think I can help."

Hewa gaped, and swung round. She could see a vague shape moving towards her. Petrified she watched. "Don't be afraid. It is I, Baruti." He sat down beside her and ran his fingers through Aramu's hair. "There is a way out of all this, if only you will follow it." He leaned back against the tree, "You know the words of God. They have lodged in your head, but they haven't grown down into your heart and your life. You talk about Almighty God, but you doubt that His strength is sufficient to help you out of this trouble."

"*Kah!*" whispered the girl, "I do not know what to think. It's all right for you to talk like this—to pray, and to say that God is near to you. . . !" Hewa waved her hands hopelessly. "On my path I meet only things of fear and witchcraft, and people whose faces are turned towards Shaitan the devil!"

Baruti nodded quietly. "*Eheh*, but faith in God is the strong spear in your hand to change all this. When God says a thing, He means it, and when He promises a thing, it will happen provided that you want to be a member of His family and travel His way, and make Him the chief of your life. Behold, life is like the path in front of us here. See? One direction it winds uphill—it is steep. The other way it runs downhill, into sand that trips your feet, and into the shadow that blinds your eyes. You can't sit here all the time, Hewa—you must move one way or the other—uphill or down. The way of faith in God is uphill, but the other way . . ."

He was interrupted by two figures walking unsteadily downhill. One of them held a long-necked gourd. Hewa clutched Aramu closer to her, and they huddled behind the trunk of the mango tree.

"*Yoh!*" she muttered, "it is my brother Dolla."

"*Neheeh!*" agreed Baruti, "and in that gourd is the strong drink that they make from honey—a drink that breeds quarrels."

A particularly loud laugh came from Dolla.

Hewa shuddered. "Baruti, I have fear . . ."

They waited till the revellers had disappeared from sight, then Baruti said, "Come let us go," and picking Aramu up led the way back to the hospital.

"You need have no fear travelling with me," he said quietly as they moved uphill, "I have my spear here to protect, and my arm is strong. In the great safari of life, when you are one of His flock, there is also nothing to fear." Then in the same quiet voice he recited the Shepherd's Psalm. In the middle he stopped. "Aramu, let these words stay in your head and in your heart: 'I will fear no evil for THOU art with me,'" He put the shaft of the spear into the boy's hand. "Hold this."

The small boy shook his head, "It is too heavy for me."

"*Eheh,*" nodded Baruti, "but it is just right for my hand. Listen again: "I will fear no evil for THOU art with me, Thy rod and Thy staff they comfort me."

They came round the corner. The lights of the hospital were ahead. Baruti stopped at the gate. "Sit here for a moment, and I will speak to the Bwana." He walked quietly into the ward.

Mosi was propped up in the corner bed and Tembo sprawled across the bottom of it. Petro had been reading them a story from the Bible when I had come on the evening round. Mosi looked up at me, "Bwana, I have words to ask."

"Ask them then."

"Bwana, why does God let people have pain in their bodies?"
His large brown eyes echoed his question.

"When God made pain, Mosi, He made it to be a useful
thing—a warning signal. Now, if you tread on a hot stone
pain calls 'Danger!' Otherwise your foot would just burn.
Stand on a thorn, and pain stabs its warning. If sand in your
eye did not hurt you might leave it there and your eye would be
damaged."

The boy nodded slowly. "*Heheh*, but God does not like you
to have pain, does He?"

"No, Mosi, He lets it be the warning signal so that you can
keep away from trouble. But Mosi, when sin came into the
world with it came disease. This brought a flood of pain and it
did damage worse than hot stones or thorns or grit. When sin
comes into anyone's life it brings twistings and trouble and
suffering."

"But can't God stop pain?"

"He can, yes. That's one of the reasons I'm here—to deal
with the things that cause pain. We can kill germs with pills,
and we can straighten bones by operations, and we can tell the
people of the Lord Jesus Christ who cures the sickness of our
souls."

Then I saw Baruti. "*Hongo*, have you news?"

"*Eheh*, I have brought a child who needs a cot, and a
woman who has sickness deep within her."

Half an hour later a small boy in a trim cot smiled up into
Petro's face. "I shall sleep with peace in this small bed next to
yours, O my father."

I smiled, "You will Aramu, but first I must *pima*—examine
your chest."

He looked up at me and smiled as I tapped the middle
finger of my left hand with the middle finger of my right.
"*Hongo!* Bwana, when you do that, it tickles."

"*Eheh*, Aramu, and this thing with which I hear the noise
beneath your ribs, this tickles a little also." I listened carefully,
and pushed him gently forward to listen to his back. He
coughed heavily, and then said huskily, "Bwana, every time I
bend like that I cough."

"Truly, Aramu. I am going to show you an easy way of
helping this chest of yours. Every morning and every evening
I want you to lie like this. . . ." I stretched across the bed

and hung over at right angles, my head close to the floor.
"Can you do that?"

"*Eheh*, but I will cough, Bwana."

"I want you to cough. There is trouble in your lungs and if
you can cough up the evil stuff that is within you then it will
help everything to heal inside."

"Bwana," cried Tembo, "You do that easily. But if Aramu
tries he may fall and hurt his head. But if I hold his legs this
will help."

"It would indeed. Aramu, how would you like to have the
strength of an elephant holding your legs while you cough as
hard as you can?"

"*Eheh*, it would be fun," smiled the boy.

He smiled at his father and closed his eyes. Petro's voice was
husky, "Sleep with peace, my son."

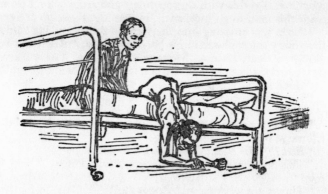

CHAPTER VIII

SECOND-HAND LEGS

"ARAMU does his upside down exercises and his cough grows less, Petro."

"Things look better, Bwana. But hasn't the time gone slowly these two weeks?"

"Cheer up," laughed Daudi, "I have news. While you were operating, the D.C. sent a special message. He says that a man who calls himself Winston Churchill Lugu, is on his way to see you, travelling by taxi."

"That's something new, Daudi. A taxi?"

"*Eheh*. There is a man in Dodoma who has a second-hand car, which he calls 'Magnificent Taxi Service'. Mr. Kolongo's words are these: Lugu loves talking. Let him talk for there are those who want to speak to him about the artificial legs that he wants to sell us."

"*Hongo!* It sounds involved, but interesting."

Daudi grinned. Mboga walked past the window. I caught his eye. "A special job for you, that will bring peculiar joy to your heart."

He beamed, "Bwana, my ears are hungry."

"Before long a car will arrive which calls itself a taxi. In it is a man named Winston Churchill Lugu. Now I want you to take a potato and push it firmly over the exhaust pipe of that machine. Do this with thoroughness and secrecy for I do not want this man to go until such time as Mr. Kolongo arrives."

Mboga was entering into the spirit of the thing. He held an imaginary microphone in his hand and said, "Receiving you loud and clear, Bwana. Message understood. The work will be carried through as you instruct, with joy. Over and out."

"Good man. Keep close."

He grinned delightedly, "I will be there, Bwana."

Tembo came up, "And what can I do, Bwana?"

"Watch the road through the hills. If you see a cloud of dust tell me at once."

"*Eheh!*" His eyes glistened with importance.

"This sounds interesting, Bwana," said Petro. "Legs for sale?"

"Things are working out, Petro. . . ."

Tembo rushed in, "Bwana, much dust, a-w-a-a-y along the road."

We watched an old model car rattle up the hill and pull up outside the hospital. On its side was written in large red letters, MAGNIFICENT TAXI COMPANY. Its battered door swung squeakily open and out stepped a rather fat, smiling and very affable man. He hurried across to me smiling broadly. "Good morning, sir."

"Good morning."

"Charming weather we have in this part of the country."

"Yes," I agreed.

"I am delighted to have the opportunity of coming out and seeing your most valuable and useful hospital."

This time I said nothing, but his smile only broadened.

"I am sure too that you will be delighted in what I have brought out." He produced a brown paper parcel from the back of the taxi. It was half as big as himself. "A little bird has told me," he smirked, "that you have need of what I have available." He started unwrapping, and then produced with a flourish four beautifully made artificial legs. Daudi's eyes were popping out of his head. Mboga took this strategic opportunity, I noticed, to move behind the taxi.

The expert salesman, who was smiling at us, dramatically stopped. His face became serious. "Forgive me, I have not introduced myself. Winston Churchill Lugu is my name. And these limbs have a very sorrowful association to me. They were my brother's, Doctor. It was very sad. He had the misfortune to fall under a train. These were made for him. Beautiful, are they not? Custom made. All British."

"Did you see your brother while he was in hospital?"

"Oh yes, I visited him regularly."

"Where was this?"

"At Moshi, on the slopes of Mt. Kiliminjaro. Beautiful country."

"And who was the doctor who did the operation?"

"An Indian doctor—most skilful man. Most attentive. But his name is very hard to pronounce. You understand how these Indian words are, do you not?"

The whole story sounded very thin to me. I beckoned to Mboga. "Mboga, will you make a deal with this man, please?" As I asked the question, my eyes fixed on him asking another. Mboga grinned, "Certainly, Bwana, and you will be pleased to know that the potato is cooking nicely."

Lugu shrugged his shoulders. "Perhaps we could sit in the shade and talk about this matter in comfort."

"It is a good suggestion, Mr. Lugu. Would you please carry on negotiations with my assistant here, and you had better use Swahili so that he may understand fully."

Mboga whispered, "There is something wrong about this, Bwana. I can smell many rats."

I grinned at him. "My nose also tells me the same story. But that will not stop you bargaining. Imagine that you have 500 shillings to spend." He nodded.

Mali walked up briskly. "Doctor, the wireless telephone please."

"Excuse me, Mr. Lugu."

"Certainly sir, certainly. I understand about telephones. Most useful, but very irritating on occasions."

I pressed down the switch, and a voice came through the speaker: "Calling Mvumi Hospital. Over."

"Mvumi Hospital. I'm receiving you loud and clear. Over."

"Doctor, what I'm saying cannot be heard outside? Over."

"I'm closing the door, Mr. Kolongo, and turning down the volume. Go ahead now. Over."

"Has Lugu arrived? Over."

"He has. We're about to begin a one-man auction sale."

"Roger. Delay him as much as possible. We're coming as fast as we can. Over and out."

I switched off the set and went out into the shade of the pepper trees. Baruti was thumbing over his ilimba. Mr. Lugu beamed. His Swahili was even more polished than his English. "Food for the ears is a very adequate way of expressing appreciation of music such as that." He turned to Baruti. "Please keep playing. It does something to me." He picked up one of the artificial legs and looked at it meditatively.

"What happened to your unfortunate relation, Mr. Lugu?"

"It was a thing of sadness, Doctor. Behold, he died, leaving a wife and seven children." Lugu registered grief.

"*Koh*," said Mboga, "is it not an odd thing to sell the bones of your relation, then?"

"Come, now," smiled Mr. Lugu, "you're talking wild words. These are legs of metal not of bone."

"But they were his legs. He walked with them."

Mr. Lugu hooded his eyes. "Make an offer. They are legs of merit. You will note there are four legs, not two. These two are ordinary legs—we called them *Miguu ya kila siku*. But these are *Miguu ya juma pili*—Sunday legs—see the highly-polished shoes, very ornamental! Yes, you agree?"

Mboga shrugged, "But to you they are of small value, except as a place for the breeding of *dudus* and spiders."

Lugu drew himself up to his full height, and reached for the paper. "Words of that sort have no profit in them."

"Legs of that sort," retorted Mboga, "have small value, unless someone wants them."

A cunning look came over Lugu's face. "They are worth more than two thousand shillings!"

Mboga grinned, "To save you from storing rubbish I offer you one hundred shillings."

Lugu took off his red fez, and mopped his forehead. "Doubtless you come from the jungle parts of Tanganyika. A hundred shillings, you say? That, to me, is merely the small grain in the cracks of the basket."

Mboga smiled. "I can see how these legs in your house are a constant sorrowful reminder of your late relation. Let two hundred shillings comfort your mind, dry your tears and weigh down your pockets."

Lugu sat back. "Hardly worn they are . . . they have been

kept with care and skill. They cost two thousand shillings, and you offer me a mere two hundred!" He raised his hands, palms upward. "I will accept one thousand shillings, not one cent less."

"Buy a pair of shoes new", said Mboga, "everybody knows that though they cost the price of a cow NEW, they are only worth a goat when worn once. Four hundred shillings."

Lugu stood to his feet, and started pacing to and fro. "Would you snatch the food from the mouth of his widow and children?" There was a catch in his voice.

Mboga's face was as hard as a rock. "Four hundred shillings."

Lugu glanced at his large gold wristwatch. He was growing restless. Mboga picked up the legs and looked at them critically. "This is a hospital where very good work is done," said Lugu ponderously. "My brother, I am sure, would have been happy that his legs might be worn in such a place as this. I will accept five hundred shillings."

Mboga jumped to his feet. "Four hundred and fifty!"

Lugu's expression was full of righteous indignation. He held the legs in his arms, and said, "There is no charity in your words. How can I soften your hearts. . . . ?" He started a long, impassioned speech about his brother.

My gaze was fixed on Tembo sitting on top of a granite boulder watching the road. Lugu's oratory was tremendous. He stopped suddenly in the middle of it.

"But I must say this—if you buy these legs, I want spot cash—here on the spot!"

"Won't a cheque do?" I asked. He shook his head.

Tembo was pulling at my coat-sleeve. "Bwana, dust!"

"The bank at Dodoma will cash my cheque," I said. "We don't keep much cash here."

"Then how much have you?" demanded Winston Churchill Lugu stretching out his hand. "Give me all that is available and I will accept a cheque for the balance."

The people crowded round. Mboga stood hands on hips, "You sell these legs of your dead brother; you carry them hundreds of miles; you drive out here in a taxi, and spend much money in doing so . . . and you want money fast, fast . . . ?"

"I have need to do this fast," laughed the red-fezzed salesman. "I am of the new way. Once it was said that 'Hurry, hurry, had no blessing.' But these days those words are only for such as do not want to grow prosperous. I am a business-man."

The cloud of dust was rapidly moving closer. At the head of that cloud was a Land Rover. Lugu saw it too. He threw the legs on the ground, pushed people aside and rushed towards the taxi. The driver stood up, "*Namna gani?*" he yelled, "What's this?"

Lugu suddenly doubled up, and his bullet head caught the taxi-man in the solar plexus. He gasped, and fell over backwards into the peanut gardens. Lugu squeezed his way into the driving seat, turned on the ignition, and trod forcibly on the starter, but the engine did not oblige.

"*Koh!*" laughed Mboga, "when you have pushed a potato as far over the exhaust of a car as I pushed that one, *heeh!* . . . . nothing will happen, indeed!"

The irate taxi driver picked up a stick, and rushed towards his vehicle. Baruti grabbed him from behind, and Mboga and Daudi kept the indignant Mr. Lugu in the taxi.

The Land Rover came roaring up the hill and stopped. Out jumped Nelson Kolongo. He greeted me very courteously, a smile playing round the corners of his lips. "Have things been happening here, Doctor?"

"Indeed they have. We have been buying legs."

"You gave him no money?"

"No, indeed," I said, "but we have the legs."

An African sergeant of police, at a nod from Mr. Kolongo, sat down firmly beside Winston Churchill Lugu in the taxi. The D.C. smiled. "He is wanted on a number of charges, that one. He is a confidence man of great skill, and a prince among thieves."

The policeman beckoned through the taxi window and handed me my stethoscope and the hospital blood-pressure apparatus. "You see what I mean?" said Nelson Kolongo, "even while he was talking with you he was adding to his collection. But speaking of legs, how much were you prepared to pay for those?"

"Five hundred shillings."

"*Koh!*" said Mboga, "I could have beaten him down to four-fifty."

"Five hundred shillings is the sum that the relatives of the late owner want for them," said the D.C. "Mr. Mabarti found them through a card record system and when I followed the matter up by the wireless telephone I heard about Lugu and the theft. He had been listening to all our conversations on his transistor radio."

"We'll gladly pay five hundred shillings; the only problem is that we haven't yet received all the money."

In the late afternoon, Petro was carefully examining the legs, admiring the skill with which they had been made. "*Yoh!* These could make all the difference to me, and instead of two thousand shillings we only need five hundred. Also we have four legs and not two. Truly God supplies more than we ever guessed."

Tembo's eyes sparkled, "See Bwana Petro, many rats are no more and I have three more shillings in my bag." He held up an ancient sock that I recognized as one of my own.

"Also there are sixty-two shillings that people have given for you. Mr. Kolongo and Gideon, Mali and Mwendwa, Elisha the carpenter—many, many people. *Kumbe!* you have many friends, Bwana Petro—and only two hundred and eighty-four shillings to find!"

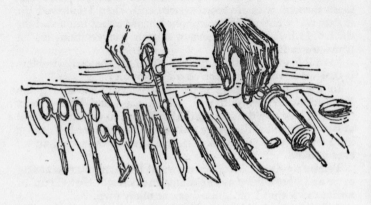

CHAPTER IX

CORKSCREWS

DAUDI and I were selecting the instruments for Mosi's operation. "Is this difficult surgery, Bwana?"

"I have never tackled anything like it before. I wish Dr. Forrest were here. Anyhow, I'll be able to do the first stage. Tomorrow at 7 a.m., we operate. This pill for Mosi at sunset, and this bottle of cough-mixture for Aramu."

Daudi nodded, "It is a thing of satisfaction that he is in hospital and having medicines regularly."

"Truly, but that doesn't mean the battle's over."

"Not nearly, Bwana. This thing will bring no joy to Miti. He will not sit quietly and do nothing."

That night sleep was hard to find. I tossed about, and then prayed, "Lord, this operation is bigger than anything I've handled. Help me."

There's no better time of the day than early morning in Tanganyika. As I walked into the ward they were carrying Mosi to the theatre. The chart above Petro's bed was encouraging. Feeling better?"

He nodded. "*Neheeh!* Bwana. But what of Mosi?"

"If I operate I may meet all sorts of difficulty."

He nodded again. "The answer, Bwana, is faith in God. You have no other path to travel but this one. . . ."

"And as for us, our work is to pray," broke in Baruti.

"God is certainly answering our prayers," said Petro. "Hewa has already been to see me this morning. In her heart is more happiness than has been there for many days. See, Aramu lies asleep. He has been quiet most of the night."

I went to the theatre. Mosi lay on the table. His voice came softly. "Will the Bwana help me? Will he hurt?"

"Today is the big day, Mosi," said Daudi. "The Bwana will work on your southerly leg."

"*Eheh*, Mosi, and it will not hurt. Come, we will pray and ask for God's help."

The anaesthetic was started. I scrubbed up, and began to operate. Mwendwa was a splendid assistant, but the operation was more complicated than I had dreamed. An X-ray would have warned me, but we had no X-ray machine. The leg bones seemed part zig zag and part corkscrew. The best I could do was to break the bone in three places and reset it, thus straightening six inches of bone. And then it became clear that to go further would produce damage rather than help.

"Mwendwa, I want to sew up now."

She looked at me for a moment and then proceeded to thread a needle with catgut.

"Daudi, prepare plasters."

"But Bwana, you haven't done much to the bone." He peered at me over his mask. "Is that all we can do?"

"At this stage, Daudi, yes."

There was a sense of defeat in the whole room. One of the nurses shrugged. "We asked God to help and has He?"

I was conscious of a number of eyes looking at me questioningly.

"He has, and He will—it may be in a short time, or it may be in a long time."

"*Heeh*!" said Mboga slowly, "I think you are making excuses for God, Bwana."

Baruti's face appeared at the window. "Bwana! Quickly! There's a man being brought to the hospital. He's dying. He's been hit on the head."

Down the hill on the far side of the dry river bed came a jeep driven furiously. It weaved its way in and out of the baobab trees and came dashing up the hill to pull up with a grind of brakes.

Mwendwa was already reboiling the instruments. They carried the injured man through the door. "*Koh!*" said Daudi, "it's Dolla! Look at his head!"

He had little pulse and he was breathing irregularly. One side of his skull had been bashed in, but there was a slim chance that he might live if we could take the pressure off his brain quickly.

In the bottom drawer of the instrument cabinet was a box of oddments that occasionally came in handy. I picked up a corkscrew, and dropped it into the sterilizer. "On to the table with him, quickly, Daudi. There's no need for anaesthetic."

The corkscrew worked excellently, and the dented-in bone was back in place in a matter of seconds. Then we battled for half an hour to deal with the damage done to the brain by sharp bits of bone. At last Dolla's breathing became regular again. His pulse followed suit. His head was bandaged and he was carried into the ward.

"He'll be all right, Daudi. Another five minutes though, and he would have died."

"Bwana, if we hadn't finished Mosi's operation when we did, Dolla would have had no hope."

I nodded slowly. "That's true, Daudi. That may be part of the answer."

We went and told Petro what had happened. "*Kah!* This is good. The work on Mosi is started; and to save Dolla's life is good. Another thing of joy—see, two registered letters have come."

I opened these. "Petro, you have two more friends who have never seen you, but have read my letter about your need of legs. One is a girl of sixteen who had polio. She says she knows what it is like to lie on her back all day, and she would like to help you to be up and active. She has sent fifty shillings. The other letter is from a man who says his legs have never given a minute's trouble and he hopes your new bones will do the same. In his letter are three hundred shillings."

"*Koh!*" said Petro, working out sums in his head. "We thought the legs would cost four times as much as they did, and

we will now have all we need and sixty-six to spare. *Hongo!*
Having faith in God works. Let us thank Him together,
Bwana."

We did. Petro grinned, "Now I must tell Hewa."

Mboga came running, "Bwana, the radio telephone buzzes."

I switched on. A voice came, "Nairobi Base calling Mvumi
hospital; are you receiving me? Over."

"Nairobi Base, this is Mvumi. Receiving you loud and clear.
Over."

"It's Forrest here. I'm still out of action, but I have news of
an American surgeon coming back from a conference in Central Africa. He's willing to operate at Mwanza. Get your man
up there fast. I hear you've bought some legs. Take them with
you. Is that clear? Over."

"Roger. I'll put Petro on tomorrow's train, together with
the legs and his full clinical history."

The voice came through the speaker. "Roger. Hope all
goes well. Any more problems? Over."

"They grow on trees here. Young Mosi's twisted legs are
much more of a tangle than we thought. Hurry up and be on
the job again. We need you. Over and out."

Daudi shook his head as he heard the news. "I don't like it
Bwana. Mwanza is 400 miles away. What will Hewa do?"

"The first thing to do is to go and tell Petro."

I sat down beside the lame man's bed. "Bwana, my blood
turns to water when I think of Dolla being in hospital. He's
a dangerous man, and brings black fear into my wife's heart.
Hongo! I'm glad these days that I am near to her and to
Aramu. When I told her about the money she hardly seemed
interested. Her mind was on her brother."

"Petro, I've come to tell you of another door opening. Dr.
Forrest has been talking to me on the radio phone. He says
that a surgeon of great skill in the matter of legs will be passing
through Mwanza on the shore of Lake Victoria. If we can put
you on tomorrow's train you will be in time for him to operate."

Petro looked stunned. "Bwana, tomorrow! And with Dolla
here!"

"Here is the answer, Petro; it comes from the Book of Pro-
verbs, 'As you go step by step I will open the way in front of
you'."

"*Heeh*," said Petro, "did not God do this for the people of Israel in the days of Pharaoh?"

"He went before them, Petro, and He was behind them as well."

"Then He will look after Hewa and Aramu. This will be my prayer many times a day."

"Petro, did you realize that the money we have over from buying the legs is almost exactly the sum we need for your train fare?"

"*Hongo!* Bwana, truly this is an open door. I must go through."

Two hours later under the pepper trees I saw Hewa, her head in her hands. "Bwana, my heart is heavy. My bones feel weak when Dolla is about."

"Have no fear, Hewa. He will be looked after."

"*Hongo!* You don't know him as I do. To have him here is bad, but for Petro to go away just now! *Kah!* What shall we do? Aramu has this sickness. If only. . . ."

She looked at me hopelessly, tears running down her face. "If only God cared! I don't want Petro to go away. Can't you work on his legs here? I'm afraid he won't come back."

"Why do you think that, Hewa?"

"Miti threw the shoes. He said Petro will die."

She pulled her black cloth over her head and walked dejectedly away.

Mwendwa shook her head. "Bwana, she's a woman of sadness, who thinks only of herself and her trouble."

"*Eheh*, Mwendwa, we call this thing self-pity. It makes you miserable and brings wretchedness to others. It is better to pray than to complain. In this way you put muscles round your soul."

Before she could reply, Mboga came dashing through the door, "Bwana, what do you know about this? Kuguni came in and had his injection and his little thyroid pills, but, *kumbe!* while you were talking to Petro no one was watching him. *Yoh-he!*" He beat on his chest with his hands, a look of ecstasy on his face.

"Come on, Mboga, what happened?"

"Bwana, anything could happen to that family."

"I'll agree with that. But what DID happen?"

"Bwana, Kuguni grabbed a bottle from a shelf and ran away with it."

"*Koh!* This could be serious."

"*Eheh*," nodded Mboga, his face very solemn. "I agree with you. I agree with you indeed, for was it not one of the larger bottles of castor oil?"

CHAPTER X

CHANGED PLANS

THE rain fell gently with a soothing sound on the hospital roof. I splashed through puddles to the ward door. Mosi lay

unsmiling, staring at the ceiling. I sat beside him. "Mosi, your legs were much worse than we had thought. I have straightened out two places, but. . . ."

He looked at me with reproach in his eyes. "Bwana, I thought you could do anything to make sick people better. I thought when you prayed to God that He would give you special strength to do the things you didn't know how to do. I thought . . ." He covered his head with the blanket, and the bed shook with soundless sobbing.

Outside, someone called to Petro, "Will you be coming to the singing tonight? Baruti has words to say."

He answered, "*Ng'o.* This evening the Bwana and I travel to Dodoma, and then I will go on the train."

"*Hongo!* Where are you going?"

"To a hospital w-a-y out to the west, near the Lake. A *fundi* is going to operate on my legs."

"*Kumbe!* And is Hewa going with you on this *safari?*"

"*Ng'o,* there is no opportunity."

There came the unmusical sound of a rickety wheelbarrow

being trundled along under the window. I looked out. "The *safari* has commenced already, Petro?"

He was perched comfortably on two old pillows in the wheel-barrow. "Behold in this taxi I have been farewelling my friend without bringing misery to my feet."

Mboga was blowing on the palms of his hands. "*Yoh!*" he said, "and being the engine of this taxi is a thing which produces thirst. I will return in a minute."

I lowered my voice, "Any news of Hewa, Petro?"

"Not yet."

"She knows what time you are leaving?"

"Yes. I wrote her a letter."

"Perhaps she will come then."

"Perhaps, Bwana."

Tembo came to me. "Bwana, Mosi has no joy, not even a little. He wants to ask you a question."

"Right, Tembo. Let us go and see him." I turned to Petro, "Will you stay here or . . .?"

"Bwana, I will wait here. Mboga will be back in a moment." His eyes turned towards the road.

"*Eheh*, Petro, the matter is understood."

At the other end of the ward Mosi suddenly smiled as I moved towards him. There was a pleading look in his eyes. "Bwana, I would have joy to come with you tonight on this *safari*, and to say good-bye to Petro, and perhaps see the train, and the town, and. . . ."

I thought of the risk. He had undergone a severe operation. "What about his temperature and pulse, Mwendwa?"

"Both normal, Doctor."

"Can you rig up a mattress and some blankets in the back of the Land Rover so that we can take Mosi with us?"

Mwenda nodded cheerfully. "Easily."

Mosi beamed with delight.

Two hours later Petro and Mosi lay side by side on mat-tresses. We moved slowly down hill over the slippery surface of wet red clay, then we splashed through shallow water in the river and as we started to climb the wheels skidded violently. I stopped and put on chains.

Ahead of us was Miti's house. People were squatting round the campfire; as it flickered their shadows looked gigantic against the red mud walls of his house. "*Hongo*," muttered

Mboga as we fastened the chain around one wheel, "they can see us." But no movement was made by the group around the fire. Petro lifted himself expectantly on one elbow. A slight figure stood to her feet. "It's Hewa!" breathed Petro. But she turned and walked through the door into the darkness of Miti's house.

I put the car into gear and we moved on past medicine man's hill on the road to Dodoma.

During that journey through the tropical night Mosi talked more than I had ever heard him do before. We drove into Dodoma, and as midnight struck stood on the station waving to Petro. The wheels of the train began to turn. We called "*Kwaheri!*"

A gramophone was playing Indian music. People from four continents were starting to move away from the railway station when the station master came up to me.

"Doctor, two telegrams have arrived for you."

I thanked him and tore them open. "*Kah*! Mboga, here's trouble. This one says to go at once to Kilimatinde—that is eighty miles' *safari* from here. The second one says that the doctor who was going to operate on Petro's legs has changed all his plans, so will we please not send Petro to Mwanza!" The red lights of the guard's van were disappearing round a distant bend.

"*Heeh!*" Mboga rolled his eyes. "But Bwana, he has already gone. How can we stop him?"

"There is a way, Mboga. Ten miles from Kilimatinde is a railway station. If we arrive before the train does, all will be well. Then we can make fresh plans."

"*Koh!* But Petro will have much disappointment."

"Truly. But God must have some other plan for us. . . ."

Mboga looked me squarely in the face. "Bwana, these days you are good at making excuses for God." He turned on his heel and walked back to the Land Rover.

Mosi sat up with blankets tucked round him. "*Heeh!* Bwana, I saw the train! This has been a *safari* of great happiness for me, but my legs—*yoh-hee*! They give pain! But they always ache in the middle of the night."

"You must have strength, Mosi, because we are now going to drive many miles to help a sick woman at Kilimatinde hospital w-a-a-y over there . . ." I pointed with my chin due west. "Sleep if you can; these will help." I gave him two pills.

There was no time to waste. We drove off into the darkness. The road was always rough but at night the potholes seemed deeper; the sides of hills looked sinister. Baobab trees loomed ominously above our heads. Once we crossed the railway line. Embers from the wood-fuelled train glowed between the rails. "*Kah!*" said Mboga, "All is well, Bwana, we'll catch it."

At one place we heard the splashing of elephants walking through swamp. We crossed a ramshackle bridge. "*Hongo!*" said Mboga, "this is the place where they say there are many crocodiles and python."

"Quietly," I said, "you'll cause Mosi to be scared . . ."

"*Ng'o*, Bwana," came his voice from the back, "I have no fear. Are not you and Mboga here to look after me?"

At that very minute the engine started to splutter. Then it coughed and went dead.

Mboga lighted a pressure lantern and hung it high in a thorn tree. From the shadows came a selection of jungle noises. Mosi peered over the side of the Land Rover. "*Heeh!* This is a place of no joy!"

"Truly. And the engine is sick. Now is the time to pray and ask God's help."

Mboga deliberately walked round to the back of the vehicle. Mosi said, "Do you think it will help to pray?"

"Surely when you've asked God to show you what to do and He does, and you find difficulties on the way, that is the very best time to ask Him to help you. He will hear, and He will help—He promised that He would."

The boy shrugged. "Well, Bwana, you pray. . . ."

I did. I told God of the difficulty we had had with Mosi's legs, of the problems of Petro's being in the train, while we were stuck in the middle of the jungle.

The night noises seemed to grow louder and more eerie. Mosi covered his head with a blanket. Mboga and I cleaned the sparkplugs and the distributor points, but the motor wouldn't start.

And then, along the track that we had travelled, came the twin headlights of a car. We stood in the middle of the road. "*Koh!* I wonder who it is?" said Mboga.

The lights came closer and swung up a rise. Then the car

F

stopped. The doors opened and two figures came towards us. A voice asked, "Can we help?"

I recognized an American medical missionary whose hospital was not far from the diamond mines.

"Dr. Martin! Well met!"

He turned to the tall man beside him. "I'd like you to meet Dr. Lindstrom from Minnesota. He's an orthopaedic surgeon returning from a conference and he's coming to us to do a whole batch of surgery."

I recognized the name of one of the world leaders of bone and joint surgery. I gripped his hand.

From somewhere close behind us a hyæna laughed horribly. "It's been quite an evening," I grinned. "Not only car trouble but look at these." I showed them the telegrams and outlined the story.

Dr. Lindstrom smiled, "I'm the cause of this mix-up. My revised plans are to go to Dr. Martin's hospital. Why not link up with us now and carry on as though nothing had happened?"

"That would be wonderful."

"Come on then, let's go. We have a train to catch."

We walked across to the Land Rover. They met Mosi, whose eyes opened very wide as I translated. Behind me I heard Mboga mutter, "God had it planned all the time. I am a creature of small wisdom to have spoken as I did."

Dr. Martin was repacking the back of his safari-bodied car. "We've plenty of room for all of you. Let's put the boy in the back. First stop Saranda to pick up Petro, then Kilimatinde, and we'll look at all these legs."

We drove fast through the African night. The jungle seemed less ominous with the headlights blazing and the engine purring quietly. We climbed up a dangerous pass and drove along a narrow rutted road with trees almost meeting overhead. I looked at my watch. "We should be there on time."

"Sure," said the driver. "Sometimes the train can be very late. Not so long ago it was charged by a rhinoceros head on. There was quite a hold-up!"

But that night the Tanganyika Express was on time and so were we. There was a very surprised railway guard and a more-than-surprised Petro, when he saw Mboga and myself.

"Come on, this is as far as you go, Petro!"

"But, Bwana, how did you get here? What's happened?"

I laughed. "Everything's happened!"

We lifted the stretcher down from the train, and put Petro in beside Mosi. Across the swamp came an odd rumble of drums, the engine whistled and the rattle of the train mixed strangely with the trumpeting of elephants.

Dawn was breaking as we drove through an old Arab town and pulled up in front of the hospital at Kilimatinde. A tired-looking nurse came out of the ward. Her face lit up as she hurried across to us. "Thank God you've come. One of the finest women in the whole place has a surgical emergency. I didn't think you could possibly arrive before midday, and she wouldn't have survived till then."

We listened to the details. Dr. Martin and I examined the sick woman and prepared to operate while Dr. Lindstrom saw Petro and Mosi.

The next two hours were full of action. The operation went smoothly. When it was over we stopped for a drink under the shade of a huge frangipani tree.

Dr. Lindstrom put down his glass. "The boy Mosi really has weird legs. We'll need to do a series of operations. His case would be incredibly difficult without a piece of equipment that I have with me." He paused, and then said, "We can help Petro more quickly. Amputation and mechanical legs can make him a new man."

"Sure," nodded Dr. Martin. "We'll add them to your list. First though, a few hours' sleep; then we can drive on to our hospital in the cool of the day."

There was the noise of a car coming up the hill. In it was the Arab mechanic. He raised his red fez. "Your vehicle should now go without any troubles, Doctor."

I thanked him, and went to pass on the good news regarding Mosi and Petro to Mboga. His eyes were wider open than normal. "Bwana, truly it is a thing of small wisdom not to have faith in God."

I nodded. "Is that the answer to your doubts? He often doesn't do things in the way we would, but He waits till He sees things fit in with His plans."

"*Hongo!* Bwana, this is food for the memory." He walked to the window. "Within me is a feeling of shame. I have apologized to God for doubting Him. Bwana, the things that have happened have surely opened my eyes."

The *safari* to Dr. Martin's hospital took six interesting hours. Mosi's eager eyes missed nothing. He chuckled when an ostrich almost ran under our wheels, and chattered to Petro about wart-hogs and hornbills and zebra.

It was dark when we arrived. One of the first to greet us was a cheerful young man in a wheelchair. He shook Petro's hand, "I'm Andreya, come with me to the ward. Mosi's bed is between yours and mine."

"That man," said Dr. Martin, "has a story very like Petro's. They'll enjoy each other's company. Now for bed."

Next morning Dr. Lindstrom started early. Andreya was his first patient. After a long and careful examination he took him to the X-ray room. Later Mosi was carried to the same place. Then we saw Dr. Lindstrom striding towards us with a wet X-ray film in each hand. He propped these up against the window and said, "That boy's leg bones would do credit to a corkscrew." He smiled at me. "I'm glad you did the first stage of the operation. And as for Petro, his condition is clear. The main necessity is to give him stumps that fit the legs you have bought. Andreya's problem was very different."

Dr. Martin nodded. He took some photographs out of an envelope. "Here it is in pictures. Right leg very bad—amputated—crutches. Left leg shows the trouble—amputated also. Wooden legs—useless. Pads on his hands and seat. Primitive travel, but better than nothing. Then came this new trouble of a phantom limb."

The man we were talking about suddenly swung his wheelchair around a corner. Perched in front of him was Mosi; Mboga followed, wheeling a trolley on which Petro lay. They stopped under the shadow of a mango tree. Andreya manœuvred his wheelchair under some gymnastic rings.

Dr. Lindstrom looked hard at the X-ray. Then he went to the window and called Andreya. The wheelchair came to us with speed. The surgeon's finger quested into the scar under the left leg. Then he straightened up and smiled. "Tell him that I think we can fix this pain in the-leg-that-isn't-there with nothing more exciting than a very small operation and some injections." Dr. Martin translated, and Andreya's face beamed.

A shout of laughter came from outside. Mboga was trying

the rings. I looked up in time to see him picking himself up ruefully from the ground.

Andreya wheeled himself back to the mango tree. I heard Mosi's voice, "Bwana Andreya, is it very dreadful to have no legs at all?"

Andreya answered, "Not very. My trouble is with the parts of me that are no longer there." He rubbed the muscles of his left thigh.

"Not only do my legs itch, but there's a burning pain in my big toe, and an ache in my left shin. Truly it is a thing of great discomfort to have troubles in parts of me that have been cut off."

"*Kah!*" said Mboga. "These pains are real?"

Andreya grimaced. "They are, especially in the hour before dawn, and in the time of rain and thunderstorms."

Petro's face was full of concern. "Can nothing be done?"

"*Eheh*, much can be done. Bwana Lindstrom has just told me that to help me is a small thing of no pain at all."

"*Kah!*" said Petro, "I have joy in my heart for you." He smiled quietly at Mboga and Mosi, "There is food for the mind in this matter. The limbs are no longer there, but the pain is. The disease is gone, finished with."

Mosi nodded.

"Remember, when Jesus forgives you, your sin is blotted right out—gone. Sometimes you will hear the voice of Shaitan accusing you and trying to deceive you, and you will feel pain as Andreya does.

"Let the scars remind you of what sin does in the way of damage, but know with certainty that the sin is gone, forgiven."

Mosi was thoughtful for a long time, then as I walked into the shadow of the mango tree he asked, "Is the Great One really going to help me too?"

"He certainly is, Mosi. He is a *fundi kabisa*, and when the work is done you will start walking like a young giraffe and as time goes on you will find yourself jumping around like a dic-dic."

The boy's face broke into a smile. "Truly, Bwana?"

"Truly." I picked him up and we all moved out into the sunlight. Mosi chuckled, "Bwana, when my legs are straight, I shall race Tembo and climb the buyu tree. . . ."

"*Neheeh!*" agreed Mboga, "and then the Bwana will have work mending broken necks!"

Dr. Lindstrom was writing in his diary. He looked up. "You will be interested to meet Samuel Mabarti, who is coming to help with the rehabilitation."

"We've met already, Dr. Lindstrom. He came out to Mvumi Hospital. His encouragement made all the difference to Petro, though I must say he pulled my leg very thoroughly."

The bone specialist chuckled, "He's done that to other people by asking which of his legs was the artificial one."

"He came to me with the yarn that there was something wrong with the blood supply to his feet."

Dr. Lindstrom laughed. We went to the ward to make a final check up before the next day's operations. He started drawing lines on the X-ray film and making calculations on the back of an envelope. I caught Petro's eye, and went across and sat beside him. "What's up?"

"Bwana, it is a hard thing that I want you to agree to."

"*Eheh*, what IS this matter?"

The words came tumbling out of his mouth. "If I told you that I wanted to give one of those pairs of legs to Andreya, would you agree? The everyday legs are all I need. Could he have the Sunday legs?"

I was silent. He hurried on. "How could I go back to our hospital with two lots of legs and remember that Andreya has only a wheelchair that is always needing repairs? How could I look at those Sunday legs hanging up on the wall on week days and remember Andreya with no legs at all?"

"They're your legs, Petro, to keep or to give away. But would you not be wise to keep the Sunday legs?"

Petro shook his head, and spoke almost in a whisper. "Bwana, if Jesus Himself were in Andreya's place would I not give Him the better legs? Are not these His words," he turned over the pages of his New Testament, and indicated a verse. I read, "Inasmuch as you have done it unto one of the least of My brothers, you have done it to Me."

Dr. Lindstrom put down his pen, and handed the tape measure that he'd been using to a nurse. I called, "You'll need that a little longer, Doctor. Petro has just told me that he wants to give the Sunday legs to his new friend."

Dr. Lindstrom took Petro's hand and shook it. "That's

simply grand; it couldn't be better. Why it won't even be a problem to adjust them to fit him."

Petro pointed under the bed. "Bwana, please pass the legs with the shoes on them."

I did so. He leaned across Mosi's cot, and handed these to Andreya. "They are my gift to you."

Andreya's eyes were wide open, but no words came. Petro's eyes twinkled, "Had you not better put them on now so that you really will have something to scratch?"

We all laughed.

As we walked through the door the surgeon said, "That's an answer to people who say, Why do missionary work? The muscles on Petro's legs may not be worth having, but those on his soul are tremendous."

CHAPTER XI

CROSS-ROADS

PETRO leaned on the back of Andreya's wheelchair as they talked in the moonlit garden. He sighed contentedly. "All the doors that seemed shut are open, Andreya—the new legs, the money for them, the journey to this hospital, the *fundi* surgeon, someone to teach me to walk again—everything."

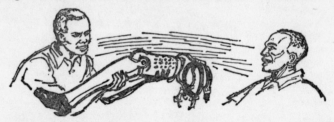

Each word came clearly as I stood at the window. I thought of the way Petro's character had grown in the last difficult weeks. His voice came again, "It will be good to walk again, and when I go back to the hospital I will be able to work better than ever before. Hewa and I will live in one of the new houses that have been built for the staff. We will work in our new garden together. I'll be close to her, and her fears will have less strength. She needs fellowship, Andreya."

"*Eheh*, Petro. Fellowship is a big thing—to be together, to talk together, to understand each other."

The crickets chirped cheerfully. There was the heavy sweet smell of frangipani. Petro drew in a deep breath, "*Yoh!* Even my leg feels less painful tonight."

Abruptly a dark cloud rolled across the moon. I heard Mboga's voice, "Petro! A thing of joy. Letters! Two of them. From Mvumi. One's from Hewa."

Petro hobbled over to the lamplight. With trembling fingers he opened the letter from his wife. His face fell as he read.

"Hewa writes nothing of all my letters. She answers none of my questions. . . ."

"*Hongo*," muttered Mboga, "I wonder if she has received them. You know what her family is like—would they not have joy in bringing her sorrow?"

Petro didn't seem to be listening. He was opening the second letter. His eyes grew wide as he read. "*Koh!*" he muttered, "the words of this letter are that my marriage will die if I let them operate on my legs."

Clouds above blotted out the moon. It was intensely dark. Thunder rumbled distantly. "God," prayed Petro quietly, "what shall I do? She is my wife. . . ." He stood there in the lamplight, his eyes fixed on his swollen feet.

Dr. Lindstrom and Dr. Martin were strolling under the mango trees. I joined them. "We operate tomorrow on Petro," said Dr. Martin. "Will you give the anaesthetic?"

I nodded. "Gladly. I'll go now and arrange for pre-medication."

I went into the ward. For a while Petro didn't look up, and then slowly he fixed his eyes on mine.

"Petro, they have decided to operate tomorrow. Come to bed now. You must be prepared for the work."

He groaned. "Tomorrow! *Yoh!* Tomorrow!" Then he pushed the letters into my hand, "Read them, Bwana. They are from Hewa and Dolla. Read them! How can I have this work done if it causes my marriage to be wrecked?"

I read Hewa's letter first:

"I am well. Aramu is well. He coughs these days with strength. The rains have fallen a little only. No work is yet done in our garden. What is your news?

Hewa."

Then I smoothed out the paper which ended up with Dolla's sprawling signature. It read:

"To PETRO,
The reason for this letter is that those of the family of Nhoto have been called together. Our words are that a man without feet we refuse, as is the custom of the tribe. The *shauri* has been made and Hewa agrees that if you follow the ways of the *Wazugu* (the Europeans) your marriage with her will die.

She and the child will return to her father's house. This is our final word. The shoes have been thrown and they speak of death."

I folded the letter and put it into its envelope. Petro stumbled across to his bed and lay down. "Bwana, an hour ago my heart was full of peace. These letters had not come then. Nor did I know when the operation was; somehow it seemed far away, but I was ready for it—but this letter of Dolla's alters everything. . . ."

"I've read the letters, Petro. I take it that this means you will lose the cattle of your dowry that you paid over to Dolla's father when you were married?"

There was anger in Petro's eyes. "*Koh!* Bwana, don't you understand at all? Cattle! This is a thing that gives small worry." He stretched out his hand and gripped my arm. "Bwana, I am sorry for my temper being as it is. But please understand, cattle do not worry me. *Kah!* How can you really understand the dark things of our lives? You see a cactus branch in the path and it's nothing more than rubbish to you. We are brought up to see death in it. Things that fill our minds and hearts with terror are matters of interest to you—nothing more. That letter is only a vague threat to you, but it tears my heart." The words came from him in a torrent. "You see in it nothing of deadliness, but I know that Hewa and Aramu will go out of my life if I let the doctors operate tomorrow. Is this the way to help my family to know God? *Kumbe!* My seeking to lose my own pain will only bring suffering and sorrow to those I love. Do I not remember how baby Lutu died in the house of her grandfather?"

He looked at me searchingly, and then speaking with desperation, "What else can I do but refuse this operation? Can you even guess what will happen to Hewa if she goes back to her family? Do you realize what will happen to the boy?"

"I understand Petro, but you must choose. Did not Abraham long ago give a choice to his nephew Lot, and did he not take the easy way because it seemed the best one for the future of his family? God has opened doors and doors and doors for you. Was this for nothing?"

"I know this thing, Bwana, but. . . ."

As he spoke I saw Mboga squatting on the floor, his face a

study. From the cot beside us came a shocked voice, "Bwana Petro! Then all your words about the Great Shepherd and Almighty God are for others only, and not for yourself? And all the things you said about my father's death. . . ." His voice broke.

"Does this mean that you don't trust God any more?" Mboga's eyes were fixed on the haggard face of his friend.

Petro ran his fingers through his hair and bowed his head. He staggered to his feet and stumbled out into the darkness. I watched the minute hand of the battered ward clock crawl round a quarter of its journey. It seemed hours later when a composed Petro hobbled back. He faced Mosi and Mboga squarely. "I believe," he breathed; "of course I have faith in God. Is He not stronger than all others? Can He not stop the hands of those who cling to the old dark ways? When He gives orders, does He not give strength to obey them?"

Mosi struggled for words, "If HE is stronger, then. . . ."

Petro spoke suddenly in a quite matter-of-fact way,

"Mosi, tomorrow they will operate on my legs, and God will take care of those whom I love, and me also."

At sunrise I went quietly through the hospital. In the theatre there was the sound of steam sterilizers. Nurses were moving purposefully about. In the ward Petro lay quiet. "*Habari?*" I greeted.

"The news is good," smiled Petro.

Mosi nodded, "And mine also."

"I have come that we may pray together. Jesus told us that if two or three come together in His Name He is there with them."

"That's His promise," nodded Petro. "When Jesus promises something, He does it, doesn't He, Mosi?"

The boy smiled and nodded his head.

Petro closed his eyes and prayed out loud, "Help us all this morning, Lord Jesus, the doctors specially. Help me that I may be calm before the work is done, and without complaints afterwards. And please, Lord Jesus, be very close to the ones we love."

A voice came down the passage, "Bring Petro to the theatre now."

He watched me putting on gown, cap and mask. "Bwana,

it's good to know that you're giving the anaesthetic. It's still better to know that underneath me are God's everlasting arms."

"*Eheh*, Petro, it is the great solid thing to know at the very bottom of your heart. Now, here's the prick of the needle. You'll be asleep before I count ten."

In due course I caught Dr. Lindstrom's eye; he nodded and started. His African assistant and the theatre staff worked quickly and efficiently. When the operation was three parts over I noticed the surgeon making careful measurements. He spoke quietly, "I think we can be certain now that Petro will be at home with the legs you bought." As the nurse put on the bandages, Dr. Lindstrom continued, "The extra week of preparation was well worth it; he'll be on his new feet a month earlier. It's a great relief to know we are safely above the active trouble."

Mboga helped me wheel Petro back to the ward, and lift him on to the bed. His pulse was full and firm. I wrote instructions for pain control, and moved across to the next bed. "Well Andreya?"

"What of Petro, Bwana?"

"Very satisfactory operation. Truly Dr. Lindstrom is a *fundi kabisa*. I've heard of his work, but to see it gives me great confidence."

That confidence increased as I watched him inject Andreya's thigh, and operate through a wound little bigger than a button hole. He took off his gloves. "That should fix everything now, and not stop him from starting to use his new legs tomorrow."

Again Mboga stood waiting to help me wheel Andreya back to the ward. "Is he all right, Bwana?"

"Yes, the cause of his pain has been dealt with."

"While you were operating on Petro we prayed, he and I, Bwana. *Koh!* He knows how to pray. He speaks to One he knows very well and loves very much. I'm sure God answers his prayers." Mboga was very serious. I had seldom seen him look as he did then.

Dr. Martin stood on the verandah in the early morning sun and nodded his head as the night nurse made her report. Dr. Lindstrom and I walked up. "Good news," he said. "Both of yesterday's patients are still asleep and none the worse for their operations." He looked towards a cloud of dust that was rising behind us. "Ah, I should think this is our friend, Mr. Mabarti."

He was right. Soon we were shaking hands. "First of all," said our visitor, "how are Petro and Andreya?"

"They are safely over the surgery," said Dr. Martin.

"Very much so," agreed Dr. Lindstrom, "but we must watch the reaction that occurs sometimes when a patient realizes that not only has he lost his pain but a limb also. That's why I'm glad you've arrived, Samuel."

I broke in, "But how did you know that Petro had arrived here?"

Our visitor smiled, "Once I suppose the message might have been sent on drums, but actually I heard all about the happenings over the radio phone."

We walked down to the ward and stood around the two beds. There were greetings in a variety of languages. Then Samuel Mabarti asked in Swahili, "*Habari gani?*"

Together Petro and Andreya answered, "Good only."

"*Eheh,*" added Petro, "and the pain has gone from my legs. Gone. For the first time for months I lie free from the misery of aching legs."

"Splendid," smiled Samuel Mabarti. "Go quietly for a few days, Petro, and then we'll begin muscle building exercises. You can watch Andreya for a start."

In the heat of the day I put my head round the door of the ward. Both Petro and Andreya were asleep. But at the hour when most people are thinking of sleep Petro was wide awake. Samuel Mabarti was with me. He spoke, "No pain, Petro?"

"No, Bwana Samuel, no pain—but . . ." A shudder shook him. I felt his pulse. It was normal. A nurse, soft-footed, came with a thermometer. There was a long minute's silence, but the mercury only reached up to the small white arrow. I grunted, "No fever. No medical trouble."

Petro smiled oddly, "No legs either."

"Truly," said Samuel Mabarti, "this is the start of a new way of life—a better way."

"I realize this," came Petro's voice softly. "But I keep thinking of Hewa. Bwana Samuel, you know the ways of medicine men and witchcraft."

Samuel Mabarti nodded. "These things I know very well,

but your great defence is praying to God. He hears and works. The best answer you can have for your wife's family is to return to Mvumi with legs that walk with the same ease as those of Miti himself. Also, keep on writing regularly to Hewa. Do not sit and think sad thoughts of self-pity. Attack. And as for worry, Let the peace of God keep your heart and your mind."

"I understand you", nodded Petro. "I am forgetting to turn things that block the way into a bridge to help me over my difficulties."

CHAPTER XII

WALKING AND FLYING

"BWANA Mabarti," said Petro, "tell us about the plans you have to teach us to walk again."

"*Eheh*. Even now as you lie in bed the legs will be strapped on. You can see how they are attached, and can understand which muscles need to be built up, and where the skin must be toughened. There's no joy in blisters!"

The legs were brought from a cupboard. Samuel Mabarti put them in place with precision, although no strap was tightened.

Mboga's voice came urgently, "Watch Petro, or he will step out of bed and walk home."

The rehabilitation man chuckled. "This is the programme." He plunged into quite a lot of detail.

I listened for quite a while and came away from the ward feeling enthusiastic and full of hope. Dr. Martin beckoned to me. "Our radio phone is calling you."

An insistent voice came through the loud speaker, "Nairobi calling, Nairobi calling. Over."

"I'm receiving you loud and clear, Nairobi. Over."

"Mvumi hospital calling, Doctor. Mvumi come in. Here's your call. Over and out."

Daudi's voice came, "Mvumi hospital calling. Over."

"Receiving you loud and clear, Daudi. What's up? Over."

There was a crackle of static, then, "Difficulties, doctor, and who can make these better than Petro's relations? First, Dolla. He climbed out of the window in the middle of the night and ran away, taking two blankets with him. This has upset Hewa. She panicked and ran away with the sick boy. They've probably gone to Miti's house. Any instructions? Over."

"Daudi, regarding Dolla, tell Mr. Kolongo about this. A man with a cracked skull like his could be in real danger medically. He certainly is still a trouble maker. Petro had a letter from him saying that if he had the amputation done his marriage would die. This upset him for a while, but he did not change his mind. The operation is over and was most successful. Try to contact Hewa and encourage her to bring Aramu back. Having no treatment can really do damage. Tell her that in a matter of say three months I believe Petro will walk into Mvumi in a way that will cause eyes to open wide. Over."

Daudi sounded excited. "Roger, Bwana. I will pass on this news and do as you say."

"Roger, Daudi. Now about Mosi, he's being built up for operation, but he's jumpy and a bit homesick. Tell you what, hold the phone open and bring Tembo, while I collect Mosi. A little chat like this might help considerably. What do you think? Over."

"Very good idea. Tembo is under the pepper trees; I'll call him. I'll leave the phone open from this end."

I hurried to the ward. A forlorn figure lay motionless in bed staring at the ceiling. "Come quickly, Mosi, I want you to talk to Tembo."

"To Tembo?" Life came back into his face. "Is he here? How did he come? What. . . ."

I carried him, blankets and all to the telephone. A young voice speaking Chigogo was coming through the microphone, "Mvumi hospital. Mvumi hospital here. Calling Mosi. Calling Mosi. Are you receiving me? Roger. Roger. Come in now please. Over."

Mosi laughed out loud. "*Kah!* That was Tembo, Bwana. What do I do?"

"Push this button and talk." I propped him up and handed him the microphone. He pushed the button.

"This is Mosi," he said hesitatingly. Then came a rush of words, "Tembo, I have joy to hear your voice. These days I'm lonely, and I miss you and Baruti and Daudi. They spend so much time operating here that there is no time to talk." Suddenly he stopped. Shyness overcame him and he buried his head in the blanket.

Tembo's voice came, "Receiving you loud and clear Mosi. We will rejoice to see you and Bwana Petro soon . . ."

A voice interrupted, "Nairobi Central calling. We have an urgent call for Dr. Martin. Over."

I lifted the microphone. "Roger, Nairobi. I'll call him. In the meantime, Mvumi, *Kwaheri*. God bless you all. Over and out."

I moved towards the door. "Lie there for a moment Mosi."

A few minutes later Dr. Martin spoke into the microphone, "Martin here. Over."

I picked Mosi up and carried him back to the ward.

"Half past one," said Dr. Martin. "I'm off to the airstrip. The Missionary Aviation Fellowship plane is bringing a man with a broken leg. Coming?"

As we drove, Dr. Lindstrom said, "I've had another look at young Mosi. The treatment is working well. I'll do him at the end of the week. His operation could take us hours. He'll need at least two transfusions—that could be tricky as he has a rare type of blood."

The aircraft came into sight, circled, and landed very smoothly. The pilot supervised the handling of his stretcher case. He said, "I picked this man up way out in the Serengeti Plains in the animal park."

"Was he charged by a rhino?" asked Dr. Lindstrom.

"More dangerous creature than that," grinned the pilot. "He was knocked down by a motor-car." He handed me a packet of letters. "These are for you, doctor. I'm going to Dodoma in four days' time. Any jobs?"

"Have you room for two of us? I have to be back at Mvumi soon. To fly would save a lot of time."

The pilot nodded. "Can do. In four days then." He started the motor and a minute later the plane to us was the size of a mosquito.

Dr. Martin swung the car round. "This chap's chances are excellent. It's only hours since his accident. It would be a different tale if he'd been driven hundreds of miles with that broken leg."

Back at the hospital I watched Samuel Mabarti talking to Mosi. He pointed, "See from one end of this passage to the other I have placed a long rope. It is knotted very tightly at each end." The boy nodded. "And are not those the rings that Andreya swings on?"

"Truly," agreed his companion. "In this way his arms, his shoulders, his back, grow very strong muscles."

The days passed quickly. One morning a nurse came hurrying into the ward carrying a tray. "Stitches out today," she said.

Following her came Dr. Martin and Dr. Lindstrom. They walked slowly down the passage looking at the rope and the rings. The surgeon tested the wire supports. "Excellent, Samuel. I can see the pattern of the whole learn-to-walk-again scheme. Andreya can swing himself along that rope and learn to balance while his muscles adapt themselves. He'll be using the new legs first, and will be a step ahead of Petro. Together they'll learn faster than either could by himself."

When we arrived at the stitch-removing ceremony we found two very excited people. Andreya was sitting in the wheel-chair. "Bwana, today's the day. *Heh!* What a joy it will be to walk, if only a very little." He looked at the rope, grinned, and spat on his hands.

A few moments later Petro watched rather wistfully as the aluminium legs were fitted on to his friend. A strap was tightened here, another loosened there. Then with our arms around the smiling African's shoulders we lifted him onto his feet. A dazed look came over his face. For a moment he couldn't find his balance. We moved slowly on to the veranda. Andreya grasped the thick rope above his head, and the weight was lifted from my shoulder. "*Yoh!*" he shouted, the muscles of his arms standing out. "I can stand!"

Samuel Mabarti smiled, "You mean that you are straight up in the air! Actually your heels are not touching the ground. Lower yourself a bit."

Andreya did so and winced as the pressure increased. Then with a grin he swung along the rope, the new legs dangling. "Gently!" called Mabarti. "It will take many days—perhaps weeks—to learn to use those legs properly. Then you'll walk as well as I do."

Early next morning they were at it again, as Mosi was carried sound asleep to the operating theatre. For four hours I watched some notable surgery. Two blood transfusions were necessary during the latter part of the operation. As plasters were put on, Dr. Lindstrom said, "Mosi will be walking fairly well in three months' time, and he'll be moving around in a few weeks. He should have fewer problems than the other two."

I went to tell Petro the news. Dr. Martin interrupted hurriedly. "Message for you from the M.A.F. pilot. He wants you to fly out in two hours' time. He's had to alter his plans."

"I must write to Hewa at once!" exclaimed Petro.

An hour and a half later when I came to say good-bye, Petro was licking up the envelope. I shook hands. "God bless and keep you both." I pocketed the letter. "I shall deliver this personally. Do not forget to write often. Hewa and Aramu need to hear from you."

Petro nodded. "Bwana, help them all you can, especially Aramu. Keep them close to the hospital. The shadow of Miti's house is a thing of fear in Hewa's life."

Through the window came a voice, "*Tayari*—ready!"

"I'll do these things, Petro. Remember, when we pray, God works."

I shook hands with Dr. Lindstrom and Samuel Mabarti. "Bwana Samuel, be specially kind to young Mosi. He will be sad that he could not say good-bye. He was still under the anaesthetic when I went in a few moments ago."

"I'll look after him, and the others also."

The jeep started up. Mboga climbed in behind. We called a final *Kwaheri*, and soon the countryside was slipping by us as we drove towards the airstrip.

From the clouds came the sound of an aircraft. "*Koh!*" said Mboga, "is it a thing of wisdom to travel in so small a plane?"

The pilot landed smoothly, stepped down and greeted us. "I have quite a day in front of me. Hop in. Fasten your seat belts."

The propeller whirled. The brakes were off. We moved over the landing strip, and then the ground fell away. In a matter of seconds Dr. Martin and the jeep looked like toys beneath us.

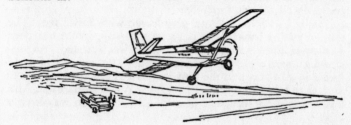

Mboga shouted questions at me most of the ninety-minute journey. He was peering excitedly through the window. "*Yoh!*" he cried, "see, the hill that looks like a crouching lion! We're coming close to Dodoma."

Below was the railway line that ran from the Indian Ocean to the Great Lakes, seven hundred miles away. The browns and greens of thornbush jungle were becoming more and more dotted with buildings, and then below us was Dodoma and the Great North Road which travelled from Cape Town to Cairo. Ahead was the airstrip; we touched down in a cloud of dust. The pilot taxied to where a group of people were standing. We undid our seat belts, stepped down, and greeted Daudi and Baruti.

Daudi spoke fast, "Bwana, there are troubles. Hewa is again at Miti's house, but is only seen outside at night. Strange things are happening."

"What of Aramu?"

"There is much talk of spells. He goes into trances and then becomes wildly excited. But always he coughs."

The Missionary Aviation Fellowship pilot was refuelling. I thanked him for the lift, and said, "You've given me one complete more day to live and be useful than if I'd travelled by bus and train."

"That's what we're here for," smiled the pilot. "Excuse me now, if I do some more of it." He stepped into the plane and waved his hand. "God bless you all."

A Land Rover swung into the road to the airstrip, and pulled up. Out stepped Mr. Kolongo. As he shook my hand he said, "I thought you'd like to know that Dolla has just been picked up near the beer market for trying to sell marihuana cigarettes.'

It was though I had been hit by a bullet. I slapped my thigh, "That could be why Aramu is behaving oddly. Hashish could do all that and more."

The D.C. nodded, "And play havoc with Hewa too. The sooner you're back the better; by the way, Dolla has been screaming threats at you ever since he was arrested. Alcohol and his doped cigarettes have loosened his tongue. He laughed like a hyæna and told me that Miti is full of envy and anger and that he hates Petro; he jeered, 'When a man like Miti hates, you'd be surprised what can happen.' So watch your step."

It was half an hour before sunset. We were obeying one of the local rules of the road, "Elephants have right of way." Two large members of the species and one very small crossed the road and went to wallow in a swamp. Baruti sniffed, "Can anyone smell anything burning?"

We put our noses to work, but detected nothing. We drove up a steep hill, but Baruti persisted. "Something IS burning."

Mboga yelled, "There is truly! See, smoke comes through the floor."

Daudi jammed on the brakes, and I saw that the oil gauge was behaving queerly.

Under the truck there was the smell of dust and oil. Daudi threw up the bonnet. Blue smoke welled out. "Look!" said Baruti. Along the road we had travelled was a spoor of oil.

"*Heeh!*" came Mboga's voice. "It's the plug of the sump." He lay on his back, shuffled underneath the car, put his hand up and then yelled, "*Koh!* I'm roasted! It's burning hot."

"Is the plug still there?" called Daudi.

"*Eheh*," shouted Mboga, "but it is nearly unscrewed and the oil leaks from it."

"Dolla's work," grunted Daudi. "He's a cunning one that."

"But," grinned Mboga, "he did not know of the spare oil we carry in the tin marked 'Antiseptic'."

It was dark when we moved on again. On the skyline I could see the contour of a hill above us. The road was like a scar in its side. "*Heeh*," said Daudi, "this place brings cold to the marrow of my bones. Even the crickets are still."

He turned off the headlights and stopped the engine. "Look over there."

"*Heeh!*" said Mboga, "It's our hospital. Its lights give me a different feeling about everything."

"Quiet," said Daudi, "listen to those drums. When Miti's wife beats drums people dance and froth comes to their lips, and their eyes become like those of a dead fish."

"*Koh!*" said Baruti, "this is evil."

Daudi spoke urgently. "Let's hide behind that buyu tree. We can see there and not be seen."

On the skyline granite boulders stood out like the sneering teeth of a skull. Below us a woman was astride an hour-glass shaped, snakeskin-covered drum, swaying sensuously. With each convulsive movement, the charms around her neck jerked, and her hands moved like the swaying heads of cobras. An owl flew overhead and seemed to disappear into the medicine man's house. As if responding to its call, Miti came through the door. He wore a head-dress of buffalo skin, and a string of leopard's teeth was round his neck. His face was masklike.

With a gesture he silenced the drums. A black cloud swept overhead. The air was filled with the strong smell of fermenting grain, and in the red flickering firelight we saw a female figure sway out of the shadows. "It's Hewa," breathed Daudi. "She seems in a trance."

Her muscles twitched. She stopped before Miti like someone hypnotised. He bent down and picked up a rooster.

"Watch," whispered Daudi, "he will kill it and will say that it runs in the direction of the one who casts spells that are hostile to Hewa."

With a sweep of his knife, Miti sliced off the cock's head. He tossed the headless bird to the ground in a way that invited it to run downhill towards the hospital. But the grim creature staggered round and careered straight at the medicine man himself, crashing into his thighs. He cursed, and flung the dead bird violently away from him.

Daudi's voice came urgently, "Let's go fast, Bwana. They must not know that we have seen this thing."

We crept back to the truck. Daudi let off the brakes and we drove silently down hill without lights.

"*Kah!*" said Baruti, spitting through the window, "darkness of all sorts brings little in the way of joy."

CHAPTER XIII

UNCERTAINTY

A<small>T</small> the hospital people crowded round us. "What of Petro and Mosi, Bwana?"

"The news is good. Mosi has straight legs, and Petro tackles his new legs with courage; but it will take time to learn to use them."

Mwendwa sighed. "Here the news is not good with Hewa. Her path has been difficult these weeks. She has but small faith, and great fear; she seems drawn to the dark ways."

I nodded, "And she's been pushed into them too. That brother of hers, Dolla, has probably been giving the child hashish and honey. This may well be the reason why he talks strangely."

"You speak truth, Bwana," nodded Mwendwa. "They have talked and talked to Hewa, and then shouted and waved their hands until she agreed to smoke hashish cigarettes. This has damaged her wisdom."

"*Koh!*" said Baruti, "Hewa has both her feet in the bog called trouble."

Daudi's voice came urgently. "Bwana, speak softly. Behold Hewa has just come through the hospital gate. See, she is coming to talk to you. *Hongo!* Already our prayers are being answered."

A dejected figure with a black cloth over her head and her shoulders hunched came towards me. She stopped some yards away. "*Hodi*, Bwana? May I come in?"

"*Karibu.*"

We went into the office together. I put a chair for her and nodded to Mali, who was holding a teapot questioningly. Hewa sat uneasily staring at the floor. She had no charms around her neck or ankles, but the first and second fingers of her right hand showed nicotine stains. She sighed deeply, and spoke in a tired voice, "Bwana, what is the news of my husband?"

"The news is good, Hewa. Here's a letter which he wrote for you only yesterday. By now you must have received the many letters that he posted to you."

She looked up at me sharply, her voice changing, "I have had no letters—not even one."

"This is a strange thing. He has written many letters both to you and to Aramu."

Hewa threw back the black cloth. Her voice was shrill, "I have had no letters! But if I had, what good would they be. He's crippled. He's useless. We'll starve, Bwana!"

She buried her face in the black cloth and her shoulders shook. Mali brought in the tea tray, slid it on to the table and put her arm around Hewa's shoulder. I poured out three cups of tea, placed one beside Hewa, and handed the second one to the nurse.

"*Hongo!* It's a strange thing, Mali, Petro's been writing letters regularly, and not one has arrived."

Hewa sat upright and tears ran down her face. "Is it a strange thing that they have not arrived? There are many who rejoice to bring sadness to my heart. *Koh!* There are many who talk bitter words in the village these days."

"*Eheh*," I agreed. "But many mouths would be closed if they'd seen Petro with his new legs, and those who have already learned to walk with ones like them. There is no doubt that Petro will be able to carry on his work here and do it better than he's ever done it before. He'll have no pain. He will be able to move faster than he ever did before. He will be able to cultivate his garden."

Hewa looked at me in amazement. Then the corners of her mouth drooped again. "Bwana, you talk about my garden, other people have begun digging and planting, but the place that Bwana Kolongo has given us has not yet been touched by any hoe."

"This will change soon, Hewa. There are those who have told me that if you agree they will have joy to help in this matter, so that your planting may go on."

"I have no money to pay them, Bwana."

"They don't want money. They're Petro's friends, and your friends."

For a moment the misery seemed to lift, but it closed round her again, and she said, "But Bwana, Aramu—he is so thin. And his cough, it shakes him with awful strength." Her tears started again.

"Stay close to the hospital, Hewa, and don't forget that you can't sit on two stools at once. The ways of Miti are not good ways, and his medicines do not help coughs of this sort."

Hewa's hands were over her face. It was hard to hear her say, "I don't know what to do. I'm being torn in two. There is the pull of the ways of God and the ways of the hospital here; and then, Bwana. . . ." She looked in the direction of the hill where Miti lived. From it came the throb of drums.

"Hewa, always remember that light is stronger than darkness. Even a small light overcomes very much darkness."

She struggled to her feet, pulled the black cloth over her face and hurried through the door with a muffled *Kwaheri*. But as she moved downhill she went slower. There was obvious misery in every step she took.

"*Hongo!*" said Mali, "there is no joy in having a double mind. Truly Jesus said, You can't serve God and the devil at the same time."

That evening Daudi said, "Four things have happened. Hewa came here and visited us of her own accord. Then she found that the letters written to her have been stolen by others. . . ."

Baruti grunted, "And who could do this but her own family?"

Daudi nodded slowly, "*Eheh*, this fills her mind with a new sort of doubt."

I broke in, "Then we have the nasty business of the beheaded rooster running straight at Miti. That must have given her a jolt. These are three things. What's the fourth?"

Daudi smiled, "It hasn't happened yet, but it will—a small time after sunset."

Later as I watched the sun go over the horizon, Mwendwa came to my door. "Bwana, where shall we put the child?"

"Which child, Mwendwa?"

"Why Aramu. His mother brought him in at the time when darkness fell."

"Where is she now?"

"*Hongo!* Bwana, she did not stay."

Daudi grinned gleefully. "That is my last point. I knew it would happen."

"Put Aramu in the corner bed, Mwendwa." She nodded, and soon the boy was comfortably propped up with pillows.

Daudi looked at him. "*Hongo!* Hewa's confidence grows in the work of the hospital, and she trusts her uncle less."

We walked up to the cot. Aramu looked scared. "Bwana, what are you going to do to me?"

"I'm going to *pima* your chest—examine it."

There was fear in his face. "You will not cut my skin with a knife?"

"I will certainly not do that. Now open your mouth wide."

The boy clenched his teeth tightly together. "No, Bwana. No, Bwana. Don't! There is great pain when they scrape my throat with their fingers to remove the teeth that grow there."

"*Hongo,*" said Baruti, "the Bwana would not do this. We do not *tula malaka*—scrape the throat—in the hospital. It is not our custom at all."

"I want to see down your throat, that's all, Aramu. Perhaps there's some sickness there."

"Promise not to put your fingers in."

"I promise. Now open wide, like Kiboko, the hippo."

The child did. One look made it obvious that his throat had been scraped recently. Quite apart from the pain, it could only have stirred up his disease. Then I listened to his chest. What I heard was a clear signpost to a dangerous advance in his lung trouble.

For three days his temperature was high. He lay in bed exhausted. Hewa came silently and visited him each day. When his temperature came down I encouraged him to start his special exercises again. "Aramu, I want you to eat with the hunger of Simba the lion himself."

He shook his head, "I am unable, Bwana. My stomach has no joy in food. Not even in the honey that they gave me in the house of my mother's relations. It tasted bitter."

"Encourage it to sing, Aramu. It is better to have songs in your stomach than coughs in your chest."

His eyes twinkled. Slowly, day by day he grew stronger. When he was able to get up he took particular pleasure in sitting in the sun on a stool carved like a crouching giraffe. He watched everything that went on. For the most part he was silent, but occasionally he would sing odd little tunes.

A week later he sat listening to Baruti playing his ilimba. He was copying every action that the musician was making, his fingers moving over the ghostly spokes of an imaginary ilimba. Daudi caught my eye and grinned, but he stopped when the child suddenly sang a weird little tune in his husky voice.

As he finished, I said, "Where did you learn that, Aramu?"

"It is a song my uncle sings."

I caught Daudi's eye, and went on, "Does your stomach have joy in the medicine these days?"

"*Eheh*, Bwana."

"And does it sing a little when you eat?"

He nodded. Then tears ran down his face. "But Bwana, I'm lonely for my father. I always have joy in being near him. His voice brings peace to my head."

Though he was looking at me, his brown eyes seemed to go right through me. "Bwana, there are those who speak with me—sometimes they sing songs. This happened very often when I was at the house of my uncle, when he gave me medicine."

"Did this medicine make you feel dizzy?"

"*Ng'o*, Bwana. I would feel brave as a lion, but my legs did not have the same courage as my head."

"Did you hear voices in your head before Miti gave you his medicine?"

He slowly shook his head. "*Ng'o*, Bwana."

I took Baruti and Daudi aside. "Two things we know—the damage done by scraping his throat was real. But worse still is the drug that they've been giving him."

"*Eheh*," agreed Baruti, "but he improves here. And my ilimba brings quiet to his mind." He went back and squatted down with the sick boy, playing his ilimba again.

"*Koh!*" said Daudi, "this is how some of the best work is done here. This is how we help many of the small ones to know God."

Next morning Gideon's bus arrived, and with it a letter from Petro, and a small square box, which contained a tape. At the hospital Hewa sat with Aramu beside her.

"*Habari?*" asked Hewa.

"The news is good." I held up the letter and the box. "And the news is here."

Aramu looked at me solemnly, "I wish my father would speak to me."

I put my hand on his curly head. "Aramu, I have an idea that he's going to."

CHAPTER XIV

PLANTING

MBOGA brought out a small tape-recorder. There was a sparkle in Aramu's eyes. "*Heeh!* Bwana, is my father's voice truly within that thing?"

I switched on. Petro's voice came clearly.

There were special messages, first for Hewa, then for a number of his friends. Aramu's face had fallen. There was no mention of his name. Suddenly Petro's voice came, "Aramu, are you there?"

The little boy beamed, "I am, my father."

"Many times a day," went on Petro's voice, "I speak to God about you and your mother. Have no fear, for the strength of Almighty God protects you. I have asked Him to do this, and He will. As I lie on my bed I think of many stories to tell you when I come back walking on my new legs. There is one about Hyæna, who thought he would be king of the jungle, but when he heard Simba the lion roar he scuttled away with his tail between his legs, for he knew his strength was small. Never forget, Aramu, that though Shaitan the devil threatens and makes terrifying noises, our God is completely strong and He says, I am with you all the day." The tape suddenly ended. The small boy looked up with a glowing face, "The voice of my father brings comfort to my heart."

Hewa's head was in her hands. Thunder rumbled.

"Do not fear the noise; rejoice that rain will help our gardens," said Daudi. "Aramu, many of us will go to your father's garden—Baruti, Mboga, and Mali, and many others. We will start the planting."

"*Yoh!*" said the small boy, "a thing of joy."

The gusty wind made the sound of drums from Miti's house come startlingly louder. The smile left Hewa's face. She shivered. But Aramu only chuckled, "Mbisi the hyæna has only fear in him when he hears the voice of Simba the lion. Truly the words of my father bring courage to my heart."

The storm was on us and great drops of rain pounded down. We stood huddled together on the veranda. Above the noise of the downpour Daudi shouted, "It would be good to dig Petro's garden in the new way, so that the water is caught instead of rushing past and taking the soil with it."

The old frightened look came back into Hewa's eyes. "*Kah!* that is not our custom."

"Truly," agreed Baruti, "but it is a good way. Have you not heard the words of the Bwana D.C?"

Hewa shook her head. Baruti held up a great cob of yellow corn. "This is the special seed that he has given us."

Hewa fumbled underneath her cloth and produced a parcel tied up in black rag. She undid the top of it, and I saw very ordinary-looking millet seed. Daudi whispered, "Bwana, see the black stuff with the millet—that is special medicine. It makes the spirits look after her crops."

The rain stopped. Everybody trooped off towards the garden. They stood in a long line and then, Baruti leading, they started to sing a cultivation song. The hoes bit into the soil, and before my eyes the rough piece of stony-looking ground became a garden. In two hours half the plot of land was dug. Then rain came again. Aramu and Hewa crouched under an umbrella watching it pelt down. Soon water was running down the path, red trickles came from their garden. "*Heeh,*" said the small boy, "the rain is stealing our garden."

"Truly," agreed Daudi, "see!" He dug a shallow trench across one of the trickles and heaped up earth behind it. The water ran into the garden and the rich soil was not carried away. "That is wisdom," laughed the child. But Hewa shook her head. We could see soil erosion taking place before our eyes, and the answer to it.

"*Kumbe!*" cried Mboga, "look down there!"

Splashing across the river came a tractor. Up the hill it lumbered. Under an umbrella beside the driver sat Nelson Kolongo. He jumped down and greeted us. "Hewa!" he called, "here is the new machine to dig your garden."

Petro's wife was speechless.

"*Hongo*," laughed Nelson Kolongo. "It has taken you perhaps two hours to dig that garden. Watch now."

In ten minutes the tractor had dug the rest of the garden. Deep furrows were drinking up the moisture.

"We have been talking about better ways," said Daudi.

"*Eheh*, a better way of cultivating, and better seed mean more crops. More crops bring more food; more food makes stronger people and there is less disease."

"*Kumbe!* and less work for the hospital," chuckled Mboga, "the Bwana would not like that."

"The more water we can store underground the better", I smiled. "Mosquitoes breed in swamps. Put the puddles underground where the roots are and they work. Turn the swamps into gardens and there is no joy for mosquitoes."

Slowly and deliberately Hewa stood up. She took her bundle of millet seed and poured it on the ground. "Come, let us plant the garden in the new way."

Nelson Kolongo nodded approvingly. "This is the thing. In the weeks ahead compare your garden with those who go the old way. You have started later than they, see how your corn grows in comparison with theirs. See it and understand. The new way is the way of wisdom."

Hoes were busily digging the soil into ridges. Aramu and Tembo built little walls which turned the water from the path into the garden. They laughed, "This is the way; when the river runs into your garden water is not lost."

There was another tropical downpour. Muddy streams of water cascaded down the hill. Children laughed and paddled. Aramu had been whisked away to the wards by a nurse, but Tembo was still busy building dams.

"*Hongo!*" said Baruti, "Never have I seen so much water held by the land. In this way we make wells of our own." He splashed round in the rich red mud. "It brings joy to your feet to walk in this."

Hewa was smiling. The corn was carefully planted. The sun came out.

"*Yoh-he!* there will be quick growth now."

"*Ngh-heh!*" called Baruti, "come over here." We looked at a garden planted in the old way. The ground had been loosened with a hoe, a grain of seed had been trodden in. The corn had grown a few inches above the flat ground, but the torrential rain had taken the soil from round it. Baruti shook his head, "The new way is better."

From all over the countryside came the rhythm of the cultivation song mixed with the busy rhythm of the hoes.

Late in the afternoon Daudi whispered in my ear, "Bwana, there is one note in the whole song which jars upon my ears."

"*Koh!* Daudi, what song? What note?"

He motioned towards Hewa. Her smile had gone, and there was a strained look in her eyes. She gazed at the ground where she had thrown the millet seed.

"*Hongo!*" said Daudi, "within her a fight is going on. She asks herself, Should I have thrown away the seed with the medicine on it? Will I bring anger upon myself for cultivating the new way?"

Mali put down her hoe. She too had seen the look on the woman's face. She put her arm through Hewa's, "Come," she said, "we will return to the hospital. It is time for the evening meal. Today is a day of rejoicing, for the harvest should be good."

"*Eheh*," said Hewa, but her eyes were full of doubt.

Baruti nodded slowly, "Bwana, I'm going to watch tonight not far from this place. There will be anger in the heart of Miti after today's happenings. Tomorrow we may find evil medicine in this garden; this would bring even deeper fear to Hewa."

Late that night I was called to the hospital. Near the buyu tree Baruti's voice came softly out of the darkness. "Neither of us will sleep much tonight, Bwana."

I replied, "Eyes wide open, O Hunter! Let no damage come to those that we try to help."

Passing the children's ward I could see Hewa bending over Aramu's cot; his cough was harsh. On the way back from the baby ward Daudi met me. "You ought to see Hewa, Bwana, she has the look of those whose minds have reached the end of the road."

I went into the ward. Hewa stood staring at the sleeping child. Suddenly she turned; I thought she was going to scream, but she clapped her hand over her mouth. Gently I gave her a pill. "Swallow it, Hewa, then go and rest. The child will be all right for Mali will look after him."

She pleaded, "Bwana, let me sleep here on the floor beside him. . . . I cannot leave him."

"All right. Do that, but lie down now and rest."

Daudi stood outside the door. "I'll stay here, Bwana, and watch as Baruti's doing near the buyu tree."

There was an odd pattern of drums that night, but Miti made no move. "Nothing happened," reported Baruti in the morning, "but Hewa thought it would. At dawn she came down here, walked around the garden, looking carefully for what she feared to find. But it was not there. When she walked back to the hospital it seemed there was more strength in her feet."

For a week the vigil went on. The corn started to sprout. There were occasional thunder showers, ideal weather for the crops. Nothing hostile happened and another week passed, but I could see Baruti losing weight as night after night he kept watch. "Miti surely will do nothing now," said Daudi, at the end of still another week.

One afternoon the mail arrived. Again there was a letter from Petro. "Mboga, go over to Hewa's house and call her: she will have joy to hear the news."

But five minutes later he was back. "Bwana, the house is closed and Hewa is not there."

"Right, I will read the letter to her later. This is what he says:

'The news is good. I am able to walk for an hour a day, although my legs wobble like those of a newly born calf. Andreya and I spend much time rubbing methylated spirits onto the stumps of our legs. These days they have a very good powder which stops perspiration in these places, for behold, you sweat, your skin becomes soft, and soon it is very sore. A visitor came here. He had a small camera, and he took pictures that move. It is a thing of interest and great education to watch yourself walk from behind. In this way we have both learned more quickly.'

And then the tone of the letter changed suddenly. I turned to those who were listening, "That is the news."

I went to the office. "Daudi, listen to this:

'Regarding what happens at home, I have shiverings up my spine and a feeling of deep fear. There is comfort to know that you and my friends are there to help. The greatest comfort is to know that the strong hand of Almighty God is upon those whom I love. But, Bwana, here, away from them, there is small joy within me."

Petro's feelings of small joy would have come to a climax if he'd been with us half an hour after sundown. Baruti hobbled to the door. "Bwana, it has happened. Where the path forks, in the corner of Hewa's garden, half buried, is a gourd no bigger than your fist. In the minds of the people this is black magic and means calamity of some sort."

Daudi nodded. "Let us go and deal with it. Who will tear the thing up and break it in pieces?"

I spoke, "Leave that to me. It is well known that witchcraft of this sort does not touch Europeans."

"That is true," said Baruti, "but it *can* mean much to Daudi and myself."

"It did mean much," agreed Daudi, "and even now the thought of touching it gives me no joy. But that will not stop me digging it up and crushing it small with the heel of my shoe."

"Not yours only, but mine as well," said Baruti.

"*Eheh*," said Daudi, "we will do this thing together. But much of the damage has been done already. Hewa knows about it, and her heart will be full of fear."

We went down the path. The small patch of light that the hurricane lantern gave only made things more eerie. In the background people, vague shadows, were watching to see what would be done; people with fear in their hearts, but people who wanted to see the charm destroyed.

"*Hongo*," muttered Daudi, "they come to watch, and if anything should happen to us, *Kah!* right through the country there will be tongues that speak softly and furtively."

We had come to the place where the gourd stuck out of the earth. Daudi pushed it over with his foot, then deliberately bent down, picked it up, placed it in the centre of the path, and ground it with his heel. Baruti stepped forward and crushed what was left into small pieces, and then, pulling a bunch of leaves from the baobab tree he swept the path clean. There was a murmur from the scores of people who were watching. On the night air came the sound of drums that throbbed on and on and on in a way that was strangely ominous.

But next morning in the brilliant sunshine, things seemed different. Aramu walked down from the hospital and sat on one of the roots of the great baobab tree. I came along the path and greeted him in the usual way, "*Mbukwa*, Aramu."

He didn't reply. Suddenly he started to sing in a queer throaty fashion. Hewa came running down the path, two of the nurses close behind her. She was trembling like a leaf, her eyes staring, her mouth twitching. Aramu made odd little movements with his fingers as though he were trying to draw a picture in the air, then he stood up, swayed, his knees crumpled, and he fell to the ground.

I bent down and felt his pulse. Hewa, her eyes wide, started the eerie dirge that African women sing when death comes to their homes. I picked up the small boy and hurried with him to the ward. As I put him on his bed his pulse became more regular, but he was quite unconscious. "Sit here with him, Hewa, and be very quiet. Drink this yourself." She swallowed the calming medicine that Mali had brought. For half an hour we waited and watched. The child was still unconscious. "Keep him absolutely quiet," I told the nurses, "but watch Hewa carefully."

All was quiet until darkness fell. Daudi came running to me. "Bwana, it's happened again. Hewa's carried Aramu off from the hospital!" As he spoke I saw the headlights of a vehicle away along the road. They swerved and abruptly went out. I jumped up. "Someone's had an accident close to Miti's house!"

We ran down the road, crossed the dry river bed and were panting up the slope towards medicine man's house when suddenly the sinister drumming which had been going on night and day stopped and the *chenga*—the alarm cry—rang

out three times. In the silence that followed I was amazed
to hear Dr. Lindstrom's voice from the gloom, "Now wouldn't
that happen! Just when I was recording the oddest collection
of drumming I've ever heard, they stop."

Baruti and Daudi moved silently towards the thornbush
surrounded house. I went over and shook the surgeon's hand.
"What brings you here, Doctor?'

"We've brought Petro back. For the last two days he's had a
strong urge to be back at Mvumi. Then came the chance to
fly and although he needed another month's practice with his
new legs, we grabbed the opportunity. I borrowed a Land
Rover in Dodoma, and here we are."

"It's grand to see you. We are in a tight spot at the moment
and his coming is a most positive answer to our prayers. By
the way, where is Petro now?"

"Asleep in the car I believe. Both he and Mosi were considerably airsick. Neither of them were taking any interest in
anything when I heard those drums and jumped out to tape
record them."

Behind us came a gasp and then a thud. Twenty yards away,
struggling to his feet was a haggard looking Petro. The rough-
ness of the pathway was no place for him to walk. Mboga and
I stood on each side of him. We moved forward to the fringe
of the clearing near Miti's house.

Behind my hand I whispered to Dr. Lindstrom. "They
were drumming out hostile spirits." He handed me a powerful
torch. I switched it on and lighted up a scene of complete
misery. Hewa sat hunched on the ground, sobbing hysterically.
Miti and his wife seemed to tower over her. Lying on a cow-
skin on the ground wrapped in a filthy cloth was the twitching
body of Aramu.

Petro's voice rang out, "*Nhawule*, what's up?"

Miti stood in front of Hewa and glared at Petro, who pushed
away Mboga's supporting hand, and with excellent balance
walked towards the place where his son lay on the ground.
"Aramu!"

The small boy stirred. His voice came shrilly, "My father!
If it were only you . . . and not your voice in a box!"

"It is I!" cried Petro, "But I cannot bend down, although
I can walk."

Hewa started to her feet, brushed aside the hand which

clutched at her and lifted up the small boy. Aramu opened his eyes, "Father!" he cried, and put out his arms. Petro held them both close.

I looked towards the house. Miti and his wife had disappeared. Dr. Lindstrom looked at me questioningly. "What's it all about?"

"Let's go back to the Land Rover. This child is desperately ill. I'll tell you about it on the way."

A quarter of an hour later we stood around Aramu's bed. Petro leaned against the wall, clutching the windowsill. Hewa stood beside him, her face drawn. The surgeon took the stethoscope from his ears. He held the child's listless hand in his and looked at the knob-like joints. "It looks like bronchiectasis and a brain abscess to me, with meningitis more than a probability. I'm afraid his chances are very slim."

Petro tried to keep his voice calm, "Bwana, what are your thoughts?"

"For many days we knew he had many *ipus*—abscesses—at the bottom of his lungs, Petro; that is why we gave him much medicine and made him cough with his head down and his legs up. The great danger is that the germs will find their way from the lungs to the brain."

Hewa spoke with difficulty, "If . . . if I had left him here, would he have been all right?"

"I think so, but this is a sickness with wicked claws."

Petro whispered, "His life is in the balance?"

I nodded. He bent down. The child's lips moved. Petro listened and turned gently to Hewa, "He asks that you sing to him."

With a catch in her voice Hewa knelt beside the cot and started to sing. The small boy sighed, relaxed and went to sleep. We tiptoed out into the warmth of the African night, leaving Petro and Hewa together at the foot of the cot.

Dr. Lindstrom walked over to the Land Rover. "I must return to Dodoma tonight. I'm flying out tomorrow. But before I go I want you to have a look at Mosi." He threw open the door. "Out you come, Mosi."

I stepped forward to help the lad. "No," smiled Dr. Lindstrom, "let him do it all by himself!"

The boy, whose legs were in plaster from toes to hip, swung himself to the ground with his arms. He moved towards us like a man on stilts. "Mosi, it's wonderful to see you walking!"

Dr. Lindstrom was speaking behind me, "We put new plasters on for him yesterday. His legs look a bit like a battlefield, but they soon will be able to take anything he cares to give them. In a few months' time his legs will be as straight as yours and mine."

He put out his hand to the boy. "*Kwaheri*, Mosi."

The boy's face was solemn. "*Kwaheri*, Bwana Doctor. *Assante muno muno*."

Dr. Lindstrom smiled, "You don't need to be a linguist to understand thanks that come from the heart. I must say goodbye to Petro."

Petro and Hewa were at the ward door. "Bwana, the child sleeps," she whispered.

Dr. Lindstrom put his hand on the shoulders of each of them. "You both should rest also. These have been days of great stress." I translated this.

"*Eheh*," said Petro, "but truly the peace of God does keep our hearts and our minds."

CHAPTER XV

HARVEST

MBOGA stood outside the door grinning, "Bwana do you see what I see?"

Up the hill towards the hospital came Petro and Hewa. They were talking together and smiling. Petro moved stiffly, and as he came past the buyu tree he stumbled over a small

root. Hewa was beside him in a moment. Again they smiled at each other and walked slowly up to the ward and through the door to the little room where Aramu lay.

"*Eheh*. It gives great satisfaction to see those two together again with joy in their hearts."

Daudi, smiling, came out of the dispensary. "It is good to see indeed, but what of the child?"

"He has great sickness. This morning he was 104°. Sometimes he is conscious; sometimes he is unconscious."

Mboga cleared his throat, "I have news, Bwana. The Arab who owns the large lorry told me that he is carrying Miti's possessions to another part of the country, 25 miles from here, and Kuguni is going with him."

We went quietly into the room where Aramu lay. He was propped up on a pillow, wide awake. Petro was telling him a story from the Bible. As he finished I looked through the window. Standing as near as he could was Mosi, listening to every word. Seeing me, he turned away, a look half of fear in his eyes. "Don't go," I called. "Stay here."

"Who is it?" asked Hewa. She stood beside me.

"It's Mosi. He's rather lonely I think."

We watched him hurrying down the path. Stiff-legged in his long plasters he tried to run, and lost his balance. "*Yoh!*" cried Hewa, "he will fall!"

Mosi fell heavily, lay there for a minute, and then crawled along the ground on his hands to a small tree, and pulled himself upright. Petro groaned, "*Kah!* I know how it feels to do that."

Daudi joined us. He pointed to Kuguni who came out of the dispensary clutching a bottle of pills. "*Hongo!* He goes downhill and out of the hospital's life. Petro, have you heard that Miti's going away?"

Hewa nodded, "And it brings joy to the bottom of our hearts. I feel free."

"This is good, Hewa. And your brother, Dolla, isn't likely to bring trouble either for many days. Nelson Kolongo tells me that for some time he will be a guest at the Hoteli ya King George."

"Gaol?"

"Yes, he's been involved in drug traffic."

"*Koh!* Then. . . ." Petro was looking towards Aramu.

I nodded. "He was giving hashish to Aramu—amongst others."

I saw Hewa looking down at her fingers. In a muffled voice she said, "He gave me cigarettes to smoke and said that they would bring peace."

There was a long uncomfortable silence, broken when Daudi looked through the window. "*Hongo!* Look at this. Truly he has courage this one."

Mosi, a grim line around his lips, was walking with difficulty uphill towards us. "*Kumbe!*" said Daudi, "things aren't going to be easy for him."

Baruti and Tembo came round the corner. They took Mosi with them to the pepper trees and soon he was lying comfortably in the sun as the minstrel played his ilimba. Seeing me walk to the door, Baruti handed over his instrument to Tembo. "Make music, while I have words with the Bwana." He came towards me, "Bwana Doctor, this is the day when you said I could go back to my house."

"You may, Baruti. Your broken leg has been very useful."

"*Eheh*, but what about young Tembo?"

"He can go with you. It is as easy to swallow pills at your house as it is here."

Baruti nodded. He went back and sat down between Tembo and Mosi and started to sing.

In the ward I examined Aramu's chart. "It looks ominous to me, Mwendwa."

"Truly, Bwana, but he has great joy. He has his father and mother with him and they talk together. Petro tells him stories and talks about God; there is a new joy in all their hearts."

Next afternoon Aramu's temperature was still higher. I heard the hum of an approaching aircraft, and hurried to the landing strip. Dr. Forrest swung down to the ground, greeted everybody and walked with me up the path. "How is your hand?" I asked.

"On duty again. What of your leg patients?"

"Petro's back. He walks surprisingly well on his new legs. But his small son is critically ill."

We walked into the ward. Through the window I could see Petro and Hewa standing looking towards the plane with Mosi between them.

Mali took us to the room where Aramu lay. Dr. Forrest bent over him, felt his pulse, examined his eyes, moved his neck back and forth. Quietly he said, "You're right. He won't be with us for long." He moved towards Petro, his hand outstretched, "What's the news?"

"My news is good only, Doctor."

Dr. Forrest suddenly saw Mosi standing uncertainly in the background. He walked over to him. "Mosi! I am delighted to see you looking so strong—and so tall! Show me what you can do. Walk for me!"

Hesitatingly the boy moved forward. He went twenty paces and Dr. Forrest's voice came, "That's splendid. Turn and come back." Mosi's face glowed with pleasure. "Now, Bwana Petro, let me see you."

Petro moved along the path. He too turned and came back. With a twinkle in his eye, Dr. Forrest said, "Good, but not quite up to Mosi's standard. You must help each other. Well, I must go; this was only a flying visit." He put his hand on the boy's shoulder, "Next time you might like to go with me on a *safari* in the aeroplane." Mosi's eyes gleamed.

Dr. Forrest dropped his voice as he moved towards the plane, "Don't come with me, I think you'd better stay here with the sick boy." I nodded. He waved his hand, "*Kwaheri*." Mosi followed him a little way down the path. Hewa, Petro and I walked into the room where Aramu lay.

"He is unconscious again."

Hewa nodded and said huskily, "Bwana, his strength seems so small. Truly his sickness increases every hour." She sat beside the bed, took the small boy's hand in hers and bowed her head. He lay there scarcely breathing.

For a long time there was silence in the room, and then abruptly Aramu sat up and looking far beyond us, said, "Yes, Great One, my father IS Petro with the new legs. Yes, my mother and I love him greatly, for he is very like You. He has often told me about You."

The child nodded and smiled as though a voice spoke to him, and then he said, "May I see your hands?" Hewa leaned forward. She was completely calm. She whispered, "He is in the presence of God."

Aramu's face was serene. "Thank you, Bwana Jesus. I would have great joy to enter your house."

"The peace of God keeps his heart," came Petro's voice quietly.

"And mine, also," breathed Hewa.

I bent over and felt Aramu's pulse, and then looked up at Petro and Hewa. They stood very close together. "He has entered God's house with joy."

Hewa, with tears running down her face, said, "Bwana, is this the end?"

I shook my head. "No Hewa, for him it is the beginning."

It was evening. Mosi was talking intently to Daudi, "Great One, what shall I do now? What will become of me when my legs are better and I can leave the hospital?"

Daudi said quietly, "You have lost your weakness and pain? You can walk? Is not this a matter for rejoicing?"

Mosi nodded his head slowly.

"Has not God arranged all this for you? And will He not arrange all the rest—where you will live, what you will do with your life?"

"Ye-e-s. But somehow sadness grips me. . . ."

He put his hand over his eyes, walked stiffly away and sat on the spreading roots of the buyu tree.

Up the hill walked Hewa and Petro. Hewa spoke, "He is there by the buyu tree."

They paused near the place where Mosi crouched awkwardly in the shadows. I heard Petro's voice, "Come with us, Mosi. There is room in our house. We can learn to walk together, and," he smiled, "we will travel in His path."

The rains were over; hot sun and dry winds had ripened the crops. The countryside was alive with activity. Through the radio phone came Nelson Kolongo's voice, "You will be having an easy time in hospital, people are too busy harvesting to be sick."

As our new link with the world at large fell silent I saw Daudi pointing. Along the path from the gardens came three people in single file. In front strode Petro, over his shoulder a sack of maize. Trying to keep in step with him was Mosi. He had no plasters on his legs, and his arms were full of tasselled corn cobs. Hewa walked gracefully behind him, a tall cone-shaped basket piled high with grain balanced effortlessly on her head.

I could hear the happy ring in Hewa's voice as she said, "Truly Mosi our corn is the best grown in any garden in the village."

"*Hongo!*" nodded Daudi, "the barrier has become a bridge for them; they travel the road together. This has been a notable harvest."

MVUMI HO

NIGHT NUR